Elementary Topics
in
Number Theory,
Algebra, and Probability

CHARLES F. GODINO

Brooklyn College

ALLYN AND BACON INC. BOSTON

To

LINDA, STEPHEN, AND CHRISTOPHER

LIBRARY OF CONGRESS CATALOG CARD NUMBER: 75–168769

PRINTED IN THE UNITED STATES OF AMERICA

Contents

I NUMBER THEORY

II ALGEBRAIC SYSTEMS

III PROBABILITY

III PROBABILITY

Preface

This text is designed primarily for a one or two semester course aimed at non-science students. It may be used in a basic course that satisfies a mathematics or science requirement, or in an elective course for students who like mathematics but do not wish to tangle with the calculus. A basic background in arithmetic and high school algebra is all that we require of the student. We attempt to use the mathematical knowledge that the student already has and build upon it.

This is *not* a survey book. There is comprehensive coverage of three basic areas in which mathematicians work. An attempt is made to take our audience as deeply as it can safely go into each area. This affords the student an opportunity to study some difficult problems and their solutions at a relatively early stage in the text.

We have selected a variety of topics from the three basic branches of number theory, algebra, and probability. In studying the number theory in the first part of the text, only a simple background in ordinary arithmetic is necessary. Many routine elementary topics are comprehensively covered. We also present some special topics that should awaken interest in any student who has a minimal curiosity concerning the ordinary number systems.

In the second part of the text, we introduce the student to other algebraic systems. We first study clock arithmetic *without* the usual equivalence relation development that is so often confusing to the student. We then discuss the algebra of 2×2 matrices and give the student a quick glimpse into a rather complicated area of modern mathematics.

In the third part, the theory of probability is handled in a very elementary fashion which nevertheless leads to the solution of some very difficult problems. The subject matter presented here should indeed be interesting to most students, since there is a natural motivation in this direction.

Finally, throughout the entire text, we try to keep in mind the level of our intended audience. In many instances, we are informal and stress examples and problems rather than precise proofs of theorems. We attempt to get the student involved as early as possible in solving worth-while problems. The basic excitement of mathematics to the professional mathematician comes from problem solving. Most of all, we attempt to share this excitement with the student.

CHARLES F. GODINO
Brooklyn College

Acknowledgment

The author wishes to thank the staff of Allyn and Bacon, Inc., for their assistance in the publication of this book. Thanks are also due to a great many teachers at Brooklyn College for using preliminary versions of this text in their classes over a three year period. The author is also indebted to Professor Francis Rush whose suggestions and constructive criticism were instrumental in shaping the ultimate form of this text. Finally, the author wishes to express his gratitude to his wife, Emily, for her patient and tireless efforts in typing the first draft, the many revisions, and the final copy.

Note To The Instructor

Much of this material, in the form of classroom notes, has been taught by numerous instructors over a three year period at Brooklyn College. Many of the topics may be skipped without disrupting the continuity of the text. We have included a sufficient amount of material to allow the instructor a wide personal choice as to which topics will be taught in a one semester course. There is also enough material to provide the instructor with an ample choice of topics to cover in a two semester course. Many of the sections deal with special topics in number theory and are not prerequisites for later sections. The sections on probability are self-contained and may be taught at the beginning or the end of the course. We feel that the instructor should have a certain amount of flexibility in making a decision on whether or not to go deeply into a topic. Consequently, much of the introductory material on prime factorization, clock arithmetic, matrices, and probability is given in sections that are separated from the more complicated material dealing with these same topics.

The following sections form the nucleus of a one semester course: 1, 2, 3, 5, 6, 8, 13, 14, 15, 19, 20. Two or three of the following sections ought to be done in addition: 4, 7, 9, 10, 11, 12, 16, 17. However, if the instructor wishes to do all of the probability in Sections 19, 20, 21, 22, there may not be time to do any of the other sections outside the nucleus. On the other hand, if the instructor wishes to skip matrices and probability, the following sections may be covered in one semester: 1, 2, 3, 4, 5, 6, 7, 8, 12, 13, 14, 15, 16.

For a two semester course, all of the following sections should be done: 1, 2, 3, 4, 5, 6, 8, 12, 13, 14, 15, 17, 18, 19, 20, 21, 22. There may also be time to do two or three of the following sections: 7, 9, 10, 11, 16.

Finally, we give a diagram that depicts the section dependencies.

Number Theory and Algebra

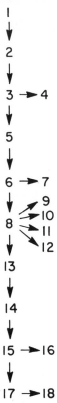

1
↓
2
↓
3 → 4
↓
5
↓
6 → 7
↓
8
9
10
11
12
↓
13
↓
14
↓
15 → 16
↓
17 → 18

Probability

19
↓
20
↓
21
↓
22

Note To The Student

We suggest that you use this text in the following manner. After a section has been discussed in class or given as a reading assignment, you should make a thorough reading of the material. Pay particular attention to the definitions, *statements* of theorems, and examples. The *proofs* of theorems may be studied during a second or third reading. There are also suggested *exercises* that appear periodically throughout each section. Whenever possible, these should be done *before* going on, since they are usually an integral part of the material being presented. The problems at the end of each section are designed to help you review the topics covered in the section, and to test your ability to apply what has been learned to other related problems. There are also some difficult related problems that have been *starred* to forewarn you. Answers to all the problems are given in the back of the text, and worked-out solutions to selected problems are provided in the Appendix. Any problem that has its solution in the Appendix will be *followed* by the word "Appendix" in parentheses.

Elementary Topics
in
Number Theory,
Algebra, and Probability

I

NUMBER THEORY

MODERN BANK CHECK NUMBERS

1 2 3 4 5 6 7 8 9 0

MODERN TYPED NUMBERS

1 2 3 4 5 6 7 8 9 0

EUROPEAN, SIXTEENTH CENTURY

1 2 3 4 5 6 7 8 9 ◇

EUROPEAN, FIFTEENTH CENTURY

1 2 3 ℓ 9 6 ⌐ 8 9 ◦

WEST ARABIC, ELEVENTH CENTURY

1 2 3 ⌐ 9 6 7 8 9

HINDU, NINTH CENTURY

ך 2 3 ४ 4 ⟨ 7 ↑ 9 ◦

HINDU, FIRST CENTURY B.C.

– = 三 Y ⼡ 6 7 ʃ ⼕

BASIC OPERATIONS ON THE INTEGERS

In this section we deal with the set of integers 0, 1, -1, 2, -2, 3, -3, 4, -4, . . . and the operations of addition, multiplication, subtraction, and division. We assume that the student is familiar with the computations associated with these operations, and we wish merely to state some of the important properties of these operations on the set of integers. The student should also recall that the set of integers consisting of 1, 2, 3, 4, . . . is called the set of *positive* integers, whereas the set consisting of -1, -2, -3, -4, . . . is called the set of *negative* integers. The integer 0 is neither positive nor negative.

The set of integers under addition and multiplication satisfies the following rules.

Closure laws   For addition: $a + b$ is an integer for any integers a and b; for multiplication: ab is an integer for any integers a and b.

Commutative laws   For addition: $a + b = b + a$ for any integers a and b; for multiplication: $ab = ba$ for any integers a and b.

Associative laws   For addition: $(a + b) + c = a + (b + c)$ for any integers a, b, and c; for multiplication: $(ab)c = a(bc)$ for any integers a, b, c.

Identity elements   For addition: $a + 0 = 0 + a = a$ for every integer a. Zero is called the identity element for addition. For multiplication: $a \cdot 1 = 1 \cdot a = a$ for every integer a. One is called the identity element for multiplication.

Cancellation laws   For addition: $a + b = a + c$ implies $b = c$ for any integers a, b, and c. For multiplication: $ab = ac$ implies $b = c$ for any *nonzero* integer a and for any integers b and c.

The set of integers under addition also possesses the following property.

Additive inverses   For each integer a, there exists an integer $-a$ such that $a + (-a) = (-a) + a = 0$; $-a$ is called the additive inverse of a. Note that if a is a negative integer, then $-a$ is positive.

Exactly *two* integers, 1 and -1, possess the following property.

Multiplicative inverses   If, for a given integer a, there exists an integer b satisfying the equation $ab = 1$, we call b the multiplicative inverse of a.

The set of integers also satisfies the following rule.

Distributive law for multiplication with respect to addition   For any integers a, b, and c, $a(b + c) = ab + ac$.

Note that the distributive law is also the basis for *factoring out* a common factor from a sum of terms. For example, $15 + 35$ can be written as $5(3 + 7)$, and $3x^2 + 6x + 12$ can be written as $3(x^2 + 2x + 4)$. Notice also that the distributive law can be stated in the form $(b + c)a = ba + ca$ since the set of integers satisfies the commutative law for multiplication.

Because each integer a has an additive inverse $-a$, we define the operation of **subtraction** as follows. For any integers a and b, $a - b = a + (-b)$. Hence, subtraction is defined in terms of addition and satisfies a *closure* law, i.e., the difference of any two integers is again an integer. As examples, $5 - 2 = 5 + (-2) = 3$ and $6 - 8 = 6 + (-8) = -2$. The student should show by examples that the operation of subtraction does *not* satisfy a *commutative* law or an *associative* law and that there is no *identity* element for this operation. On the other hand, the *distributive* law for multiplication with respect to subtraction is valid and *cancellation* laws for subtraction also hold (see Problems 1.3 and 1.4).

We finally come to the operation of **division** on the set of integers. If a is any integer and b is any nonzero integer, we define a divided by b, written $a \div b$, to be that integer c where $a = bc$ *provided* such an integer c exists. For example, $8 \div 4 = 2$ since $8 = 4 \cdot 2$, while $4 \div 8$ does not exist in the set of integers since there exists no integer c such that $4 = 8c$. Consequently, it is not true that a divided by b is always an integer whenever a and b are integers. Observe that $a \div 1 = a$ for every integer a since $a = 1 \cdot a$, and $a \div a = 1$ for every nonzero integer a since $a = a \cdot 1$.

Note also that *division* by *zero* is left undefined, since if $a \neq 0$, $a \div 0 = c$ implies $a = 0 \cdot c = 0$ and this is *not* possible for any integer c since $a \neq 0$. On the other hand, if $a = 0$, we obtain $0 \div 0 = c$ which implies $0 = 0 \cdot c = 0$. The last equation is satisfied by *every* integer c and thus $0 \div 0$ still cannot be defined.

As exercises, show by examples that none of the rules and properties mentioned at the beginning of this section is valid in the set of integers under the operation of division except for *cancellation* laws (see Problem 1.5).

As another exercise, prove the following statement using the definition of division and the cancellation law for multiplication: in the definition of division, when the integer c exists, it is *unique*, i.e., if $a \div b = c$ and $a \div b = d$, then $c = d$.

Most of the preceding rules and properties should be clear to the student. However, there are other number systems and algebraic systems in which some of these rules and properties do not hold. We shall study some of these systems later and, at that time, Section 1 will be useful as a reference.

PROBLEMS

1.1 (a) Prove that $a \cdot 0 = 0$ for every integer a. (*Hint.* Write $a = a(1 + 0)$ and use the distributive law and cancellation law.)

(b) Prove that $ab = 0$ implies either $a = 0$ or $b = 0$.

(c) Prove that $(-1)a = -a$ for every integer a.

1.2 Prove each of the following rules of signs for any integers a and b.

(a) $-(-a) = a$

(b) $(-a)b = -(ab)$

(c) $a(-b) = -(ab)$

(d) $(-a)(-b) = ab$

1.3 Prove the distributive law for multiplication with respect to subtraction: for any integers a, b, and c, $a(b - c) = ab - ac$.

1.4 Prove the following cancellation laws for subtraction.

(a) For any integers a, b, and c, $a - b = a - c$ implies $b = c$ (Appendix).

(b) For any integers a, b, and c, $a - c = b - c$ implies $a = b$.

1.5 Prove the following cancellation laws for division.

(a) For any nonzero integers a, b, and c, $a \div b = a \div c$ implies $b = c$ (Appendix).

(b) For any nonzero integers a, b, and c, $a \div c = b \div c$ implies $a = b$.

1.6 On the set of *positive* integers, define the operation $a * b = a^b$. For example, $2 * 3 = 2^3 = 8$ and $5 * 2 = 5^2 = 25$. Does the set of positive integers under the operation $*$ satisfy
   (a)   a closure law
   (b)   a commutative law
   (c)   an associative law
   (d)   the identity element property?

1.7 A *rational number* or *fraction* is a number of the form p/q where p is any integer and q is any *nonzero* integer; p is called the numerator and q is called the denominator. Two fractions a/b and c/d are equal if and only if $ad = bc$; for example, $2/3 = 6/9$ since $2 \cdot 9 = 3 \cdot 6$, while $3/4 \neq 5/8$ since $3 \cdot 8 \neq 4 \cdot 5$. We define the following operations on the set of rational numbers. For any two rational numbers a/b and c/d,

$$\text{Addition} \quad \frac{a}{b} + \frac{c}{d} = \frac{ad + bc}{bd}$$

$$\text{Multiplication} \quad \frac{a}{b} \cdot \frac{c}{d} = \frac{ac}{bd}$$

$$\text{Subtraction} \quad \frac{a}{b} - \frac{c}{d} = \frac{ad - bc}{bd}$$

$$\text{Division} \quad \frac{a}{b} \div \frac{c}{d} = \frac{ad}{bc} \text{ provided } c \neq 0.$$

Observe that each integer p is associated with the rational number $p/1$ and therefore every integer is a rational number with denominator equal to 1. Prove each of the following results.
   (a)   The rational numbers satisfy closure laws for addition, multiplication, subtraction, *and* nonzero division.
   (b)   The rational numbers satisfy commutative and associative laws for addition and multiplication.
   (c)   The rationals have an additive and a multiplicative identity element.
   (d)   Every rational number has an additive inverse and every *nonzero* rational number has a multiplicative inverse.

1.8 Let A represent the closure property for addition;

   B, the closure property for multiplication;

   C, the closure property for subtraction;

   D, the identity property for addition;

   E, the identity property for multiplication;

   F, the inverse property for addition;

   G, the inverse property for multiplication.

Determine which of the preceding properties hold in each of the following systems:
   1.   the even integers
   2.   the odd integers
   3.   the positive integers
   4.   the nonnegative integers

5. the negative integers
6. the set of all multiples of 5
7. the set of all fractions
8. the set of all nonzero fractions
9. the set consisting of the integers 0, 1, and −1
10. the set consisting of the integers 1 and −1.

Section 2

ORDER AXIOMS

The student already has an idea of order and we wish to build upon it. For example, 5 is less than 6, 10 is less than 15, -7 is less than -5, etc. The basic idea in comparing two integers involves seeing which one must be increased in order to obtain the other. This integer will be the *smaller* of the two. In the preceding examples, 5 is less than 6 since $5 + 1 = 6$, 10 is less than 15 since $10 + 5 = 15$, and -7 is less than -5 since $-7 + 2 = -5$. Consequently, we say that an integer a is *less than* an integer b (in symbols $a < b$) if there exists a *positive* integer x such that $a + x = b$. We may also say that b is *greater than a* (in symbols $b > a$).

PROPERTIES

1. For any two integers a and b, one and only one of the following relations holds: $a = b, a < b, a > b$.

2. For any integers a, b, and c, if $a < b$ and $b < c$, then $a < c$.

    We can verify that this property holds by the following argument.

    If $a < b$, there exists a positive integer x such that $a + x = b$. If $b < c$, there exists a positive integer y such that $b + y = c$. Substituting for b in the second equation its value from the first equation, we obtain

$$(a + x) + y = a + (x + y) = c \,.$$

8

But x and y are both positive integers; therefore, $x + y$ is a positive integer z. Consequently, the last equation can be written as $a + z = c$, where z is a positive integer. Hence, $a < c$ and the proof is complete.

The Well-Ordering Axiom—Every set of positive integers containing at least one integer has a smallest or least integer. The meaning of the Well-Ordering Axiom should be clear and we justify the acceptance of the axiom in the following way. If S is a set of positive integers, then either 1 is in S or 1 is not in S. If 1 is in S, then 1 is certainly the least integer in S; if 1 is not in S, we go on to the integer 2. If 2 is in S, then 2 is the least integer in S; if 2 is not in S, we go on to the integer 3. If we continue this process, eventually we will come to an integer n in S (since S has at least one integer) with the property that no integer $k < n$ is in S; the integer n will then be the least integer in S.

Observe that the Well-Ordering Axiom also could be stated for sets of *nonnegative* integers since, if 0 is in S, it is the least integer since $0 < x$ for every positive integer x. If 0 is not in S, then S is again a set of positive integers and the axiom is valid in the original form.

> These three properties should seem rather obvious to most students. However, they are essential ingredients for the study of order relations among integers. Therefore, we state them here so that we may have them as a handy reference later on. In particular, the Well-Ordering Axiom turns out to be very useful as a tool in proving many of the more important theorems in this text and in more advanced texts in mathematics as well.

PROBLEMS

2.1 Prove each of the following:
    (a) if $a < b$ and c is any integer, then $a + c < b + c$
    (b) if $a < b$ and c is any *positive* integer, then $ac < bc$
    (c) if $a < b$ and c is any *negative* integer, then $ac > bc$ (Appendix).

2.2 Let T be any set of integers containing at least one integer. Show that if T contains at most a finite number of negative integers, T has a least integer.

2.3 Show that each of the following sets does *not* have a least number. Does this contradict the Well-Ordering Axiom?
    (a) $1, -1, 3, -3, 5, -5, 7, -7, \ldots$
    (b) $1, 1/2, 1/3, 1/4, 1/5, 1/6, 1/7, \ldots$
    (c) $.1, .01, .001, .0001, .00001, .000001, \ldots$

2.4 Find the least positive integer in each of the following sets:
    (a) the set of all integers of the form $13 - 2x$ where x is an integer

(b) the set of all integers of the form $37 - 7x$ where x is an integer

(c) the set of all integers of the form $937 - 41x$ where x is an integer.

2.5 Find the least nonnegative integer in each of the following sets:

(a) the set of all integers of the form $39 - 8x$

(b) the set of all integers of the form $35 - 5x$

(c) the set of all integers of the form $851 - 23x$.

Section 3

THEOREMS ON DIVISION

In this section, we state and prove some elementary theorems on the division of integers. We shall need these results in many of the later sections. The most important theorem in this section is the Division Algorithm, which justifies the process of long division. In the proof of the Division Algorithm, we use the Well-Ordering Axiom of the preceding section.

Terminology: whenever $a = cx$ for integers a, x, and c, we say that c divides a (or x divides a) and we call c and x *factors* or *divisors* of a, while a is called a *multiple* of c or x. For example, $10 = 2 \cdot 5$; hence, 2 and 5 are factors or divisors of 10, while 10 is a multiple of 5, namely $2 \cdot 5$, or 10 is a multiple of 2, namely $5 \cdot 2$.

In what follows, all letters represent integers.

3.1 Theorem   If c divides a, then c divides ab for any integer b.

Proof c divides a implies there exists an integer x such that $a = cx$. But $ab = (cx)b = c(xb) = cz$ where z is the integer xb. Now $ab = cz$ implies c divides ab.

3.2 Theorem   If c divides a and c divides b, then c divides $a + b$ and $a - b$.

Proof c divides a implies $a = cx$ for some integer x. c divides b implies $b = cy$ for some integer y. Therefore, $a + b = cx + cy = c(x + y) =$

11

cz where z is the integer $x + y$. Now $a + b = cz$ implies c divides $a + b$. Similarly, $a - b = cx - cy = c(x - y) = cw$ where w is the integer $x - y$, and thus c divides $a - b$.

3.3 Theorem   If c divides a and c divides b, then c divides $aj + bk$ for any two integers j and k.

The proof follows directly from the preceding two theorems and is left as an exercise for the student.

3.4 Theorem   If $a = n + b$ and c divides both a and b, then c divides n.

Proof If $a = n + b$, then $n = a - b$. Now c divides a and b so we simply apply Theorem 3.2.

3.5 Theorem   If c divides a and a divides b, then c divides b.

The proof is left as an exercise.

3.6 Theorem
**The Division
Algorithm**

Let a and b be two positive integers with $a > b$. Then there exist unique integers q and r such that $a = bq + r$, where $0 \le r < b$; q is called the quotient, r the remainder, b the divisor, and a the dividend.

Before proving this result, we give a few examples.

1. Let $a = 13, b = 2$, then $q = 6, r = 1$, and we have $13 = 2 \cdot 6 + 1$.
2. Let $a = 37, b = 7$, then $q = 5, r = 2$, and $37 = 7 \cdot 5 + 2$.
3. Let $a = 937, b = 41$, then $q = 22, r = 35$, and $937 = 41 \cdot 22 + 35$.
4. Let $a = 35, b = 5$, then $q = 7, r = 0$, and $35 = 5 \cdot 7 + 0 = 5 \cdot 7$.

Proof Consider the set of *nonnegative* integers of the form $\{a - bx\}$ where x is an integer. Clearly, this set contains at least one positive integer, namely $a - b$ (when $x = 1$), since $a > b$ is given. Therefore, we may apply the Well-Ordering Axiom and obtain the least nonnegative integer in the set $\{a - bx\}$. Let q be the value of x that yields the least nonnegative integer and let r be the least nonnegative integer. Then $a - bq = r$ and $a = bq + r$.

Hence, we have now proved the *existence* of q and r; however, we must still show that $0 \le r < b$. We know $r \ge 0$ since r is the least nonnegative integer in the set $\{a - bx\}$. Also, $r < b$ since $r \ge b$ implies the existence of a nonnegative integer k such that $r = b + k$. Then $a = bq + r = bq + b + k = b(q + 1) + k$. Therefore, $a - b(q + 1) = k$ is a nonnegative integer in $\{a - bx\}$ with $x = q + 1$. But $a - b(q + 1) < a - bq = r$, which contradicts the fact that r is the least nonnegative integer in the set $\{a - bx\}$. Thus, we have found integers q and r that satisfy the given condition.

As examples, if $a = 13$, $b = 2$, then for $x = 1, 2, 3, 4, 5, 6$ we obtain $\{13 - 2x\} = \{11, 9, 7, 5, 3, 1\}$ where $r = 1 = $ the least nonnegative integer and $q = 6$; if $a = 37$, $b = 7$, then for $x = 1, 2, 3, 4, 5$ we obtain $\{37 - 7x\} = \{30, 23, 16, 9, 2\}$ where $r = 2 = $ the least nonnegative integer and $q = 5$; if $a = 35$, $b = 5$, then for $x = 1, 2, 3, 4, 5, 6, 7$ we obtain $\{35 - 5x\} = \{30, 25, 20, 15, 10, 5, 0\}$ where $r = 0 = $ the least nonnegative integer and $q = 7$.

Finally, to complete the proof of the theorem, we must show that q and r are *unique*. Now suppose there exist other integers q' and r' with $a = bq' + r'$ where $0 \le r' < b$. Then $a = bq + r = bq' + r'$. Suppose $r \ge r'$, then $bq + r = bq' + r'$ implies $0 \le r - r' = bq' - bq = b(q' - q)$. This leads to $0 \le r - r' = b(q' - q)$, which implies that $q' - q \ge 0$ (since $b > 0$). But $0 \le r < b$ and $0 \le r' < b$ imply that $r - r' < b$. Therefore, the preceding equation gives $b(q' - q)$ as a multiple of b that is greater than or equal to zero and less than b. This implies that $b(q' - q)$ *must* be zero and so $q' - q$ and $r - r'$ are both zero. Hence, $q' = q$ and $r' = r$ and we have shown the uniqueness.

As a final remark, we mention that the Division Algorithm is valid in a more general situation with the following initial condition: *a and b any two integers with $b \ne 0$*. The proof in this more general form is more complicated than the one presented in the text. It yields the result that q and r are unique integers with $0 \le r < b$ if $b > 0$, or $0 \le r < -b$ if $b < 0$. As examples of the Division Algorithm in the more general form, consider the following choices for a and b.

1. Let $a = -13$, $b = 2$, then $q = -7$, $r = 1$, and we have $-13 = 2(-7) + 1$.
2. Let $a = 37$, $b = -7$, then $q = -5$, $r = 2$, and $37 = (-7)(-5) + 2$.
3. Let $a = -37$, $b = -2$, then $q = 19$, $r = 1$, and $-37 = (-2)(19) + 1$.

As exercises, verify that in each of the three preceding examples, r satisfies either the condition $0 \le r < b$ or the condition $0 \le r < -b$.

PROBLEMS

3.1 Express 12 as a multiple of each of the integers 1, 2, 3, 4, 6, and 12.

3.2 Express 72 as a multiple of each of the integers 1, 2, 3, 4, 6, 8, 12, 18, 36, and 72.

3.3 Using the Division Algorithm, determine integers q and r for each of the following pairs of integers.

(a) $a = 97, b = 43$ (b) $a = 171, b = 133$
(c) $a = 247, b = 26$ (d) $a = 413, b = 273$
(e) $a = 1066, b = 273$ (f) $a = 996, b = 225$

3.4 (a) If an integer n is divided by 5, what are the only possible remainders?

(b) If an integer n is divided by 7, what are the only possible remainders?

(c) If an integer n is divided by 2, what are the only possible remainders?

3.5 *Definition.* An integer n is *even* if upon division by 2, it yields a remainder of zero, i.e., $n = 2q$ for some integer q.

Definition. An integer n is *odd* if upon division by 2, it yields a remainder of 1, i.e., $n = 2q + 1$ for some integer q. Prove each of the following results.

(a) 0 is an even integer.
(b) 1 is an odd integer.
(c) The set of all *even* integers is *closed* under addition and multiplication.
(d) The set of all *odd* integers is *closed* under multiplication.
(e) The sum of an odd integer and an even integer is *always* odd.
(f) The product of an odd integer and an even integer is *always* even.

3.6 *Definition.* An integer greater than 1 is called a *prime* if its only positive divisors are 1 and itself. Prove that the only *even* prime is 2.

3.7 Show that for any positive integer n, the product $n(n + 1)(n + 2)$ is divisible by 6; also show that the product $n(n + 1)(2n + 1)$ is divisible by 6 (Appendix).

3.8* (a) Show that the product of any five consecutive positive integers is divisible by 60.

(b) Show that the product of any seven consecutive positive integers is divisible by 2520.

Section 4

NUMBERS TO DIFFERENT BASES

We assume that the student is familiar with the decimal system to the extent that he knows how to write an integer in the long form as a *sum of multiples of powers of 10.* For example, $278 = 2(10^2) + 7(10) + 8$, $5243 = 5(10^3) + 2(10^2) + 4(10) + 3$, and $27935 = 2(10^4) + 7(10^3) + 9(10^2) + 3(10) + 5$. In general, any integer n with $k + 1$ digits can be written in the form $n = c_k 10^k + c_{k-1} 10^{k-1} + \ldots + c_2 10^2 + c_1 10 + c_0$ where $0 < c_k \leq 9$ and $0 \leq c_i \leq 9$ for each $i = 0, 1, 2, \ldots, k - 1$.

Using the Division Algorithm, we will now exhibit a method that enables us to write integers in a *non-decimal* system, that is, a system in which the integers are expressed as a *sum of multiples of powers of numbers other than 10.* For example, let us write 278 as a *sum of multiples of powers of 7,* that is, *in the base 7.* When 278 is written in the base 7, it will have the form $278 = a \cdot 7^2 + b \cdot 7 + c$ where a, b, and c are integers with $0 \leq b$, $c < 7$ and $0 < a < 7$ (since $7^2 = 49 < 278 < 343 = 7^3$). The Division Algorithm guarantees a unique quotient and remainder when we divide 278, or any expression equal to it, by 7. Below we exhibit the process that determines the coefficients a, b, and c. We divide by 7 and equate quotients and remainders. We then divide the quotients by 7 and equate the new quotients and remainders, and so on, until we obtain the coefficients a, b, and c.

We begin with $a \cdot 7^2 + b \cdot 7 + c = 278$. Dividing both sides of this equation by 7 and equating the remainders and the quotients, we obtain $c = 5$ and $a \cdot 7 + b = 39$. Dividing both sides of the last equation by 7 and equating the remainders and the quotients, we arrive at $b = 4$ and $a = 5$. Consequently, $278 = 5 \cdot 7^2 + 4 \cdot 7 + 5$, which can be written more simply as $(545)_7$. The latter form is a short way of writing numbers in the base 7.

As another example, let us write 278 as a *sum of multiples of powers of 5*, that is, *in the base 5*. It will have the form $a \cdot 5^3 + b \cdot 5^2 + c \cdot 5 + d$ where a, b, c, and d are integers with $0 \leq b, c, d < 5$ and $0 < a < 5$ (since $5^3 = 125 < 278 < 625 = 5^4$). Therefore, we begin with $a \cdot 5^3 + b \cdot 5^2 + c \cdot 5 + d = 278$, and we divide both sides of this equation by 5. We then equate the remainders and the quotients and obtain $d = 3$ and $a \cdot 5^2 + b \cdot 5 + c = 55$. Dividing both sides of the last equation by 5 and equating the remainders and the quotients, we arrive at $c = 0$ and $a \cdot 5 + b = 11$. We then divide both sides of the last equation by 5, equate the remainders and the quotients, and obtain $b = 1$ and $a = 2$. Consequently, $278 = 2 \cdot 5^3 + 1 \cdot 5^2 + 0 \cdot 5 + 3 = (2103)_5$. The latter form is a short way of writing numbers in the base 5.

Finally, to write 278 in the base 2, we need an expression of the form $a \cdot 2^8 + b \cdot 2^7 + c \cdot 2^6 + d \cdot 2^5 + e \cdot 2^4 + f \cdot 2^3 + g \cdot 2^2 + h \cdot 2 + i$ (since $2^8 = 256 < 278 < 512 = 2^9$). If the student imitates the process exhibited in the preceding two examples, he will obtain 278 in the base 2 as $(100010110)_2$.

To assist you in gaining a clearer idea of the results obtained in the preceding examples, suppose a gambling casino owes you $278. Suppose further that (1) the casino has red chips worth $100 each, white chips worth $10 each, and blue chips worth $1 each and that (2) it will not pay you with more than 9 chips of any one color. Then it must pay you with 2 red, 7 white, and 8 blue chips. This corresponds to the number 278 in the decimal system. If instead we suppose that (1) the casino has red chips worth $49 each, white chips worth $7 each, and blue chips worth $1 each, and that (2) it will not pay you with more than 6 chips of any one color, then it must pay you with 5 red, 4 white, and 5 blue chips. This corresponds to the base 7 representation of 278 as $(545)_7$. Now suppose that (1) the casino has red chips worth $125 each, white chips worth $25 each, blue chips worth $5 each, and green chips worth $1 each, and that (2) it will not pay you with more than 4 chips of any one color. Then it must pay $278 with 2 red, 1 white, and 3 green chips. This corresponds to the representation of 278 in the base 5 as $(2103)_5$. Finally, as an exercise, compute the number and the denominations of the chips required to pay you $278 in a way that corresponds to the base 2 representation of 278.

In each of the preceding examples, you receive the same amount of money. It is simply the *denominations* of the chips that determine the number and the color of the chips in the payoff. Hence, when we write a decimal integer in another base, it is the *same* integer under a *new* representation brought about by a change in the *denominations* of the powers used to write the number.

The following theorem establishes the fact that if d is any positive integer greater than 1 and n is any integer, then n can be written in the base d, that is, n can be written as a sum of multiples of powers of d.

4.1 Theorem

The Bases Theorem

Let n and d be positive integers with $1 < d$. Then, n can be written in the form $n = c_k d^k + c_{k-1} d^{k-1} + \ldots + c_2 d^2 + c_1 d + c_0$ where c_0, c_1, $c_2, \ldots, c_k$ are unique nonnegative integers less than d with $c_k \neq 0$.

Proof Clearly, if $n < d$, then $n = c_0$, and if $n = d$, then $n = 1 \cdot d + 0 = (10)_d$. Now suppose there exists an integer $m > d$ that *cannot* be written in the base d. Let S be the set of all such integers. By the Well-Ordering Axiom, S has a least integer $a > d$. We divide a by d and obtain (by the Division Algorithm) unique integers q and r such that $a = dq + r$ where $0 \leq r < d$ and $1 \leq q < a$ (since $a > d$, and a is r *plus* a positive multiple of q). Now, if $q < d$, then $a = dq + r = (qr)_d$ is a representation of a in the base d contradicting the fact that a is in S (remember, S is the set of all integers that *cannot* be written in the base d). If $q = d$, then $a = d^2 + r = (10r)_d$, again contradicting the fact that a is in S. Now suppose $d < q < a$. Then q can be expressed in the base d (since $q < a$ and a is the *least* integer that cannot be expressed in the base d). Hence, for some positive integer k, $q = c_k d^{k-1} + c_{k-1} d^{k-2} + \ldots + c_2 d + c_1$ where $0 < c_k < d$ and $0 \leq c_i < d$ for $i = 1$, 2, 3,$\ldots, k - 1$. *Multiplying* this expression for q by d and *adding* r, we obtain $a = dq + r = c_k d^k + c_{k-1} d^{k-1} + \ldots + c_2 d^2 + c_1 d + r$. Finally, if we let $r = c_0$, we have an expression for a in the base d. This again contradicts the fact that a is in the set S. Therefore, we reach a contradiction in *every* case stemming from our selection of a as the *least* integer in S. Hence S has *no least integer* and must therefore contain *no positive integers* at all. (Remember, the Well-Ordering Axiom states that if a set S has positive integers, it must have a least positive integer.) Consequently, every positive integer n *can* be written in the base d.

To prove the *uniqueness* of the representation, we proceed as follows. Suppose there are *two* representations of an integer n in the base d. Then for some positive integer k and some nonnegative integer j, there exist nonnegative integers $c_k, c_{k-1}, \ldots, c_2, c_1, c_0$, and $c'_{k+j}, c'_{k+j-1}, \ldots,$ $c'_k, \ldots, c'_2, c'_1, c'_0$ all of which are less than d such that $c_k d^k + c_{k-1} d^{k-1} + \ldots + c_2 d^2 + c_1 d + c_0 = n = c'_{k+j} d^{k+j} + c'_{k+j-1} d^{k+j-1} + \ldots + c'_k d^k + \ldots + c'_2 d^2 + c'_1 d + c'_0$. Again, using the Division Algorithm, we divide both of the expressions for n by d and obtain equal quotients and equal remainders. But c_0 is the remainder of the first expression for n while c_0' is the remainder of the second expression for n. Therefore, $c_0' = c_0$ and the two equal quotients can be divided by d, yielding remainders c_1' and c_1, respectively. Therefore, $c_1' = c_1$ and the two new quotients may be divided by d, yielding the remainders c_2' and c_2, respectively. Hence, $c_2' = c_2$ and we continue in this fashion, obtaining $c_3' = c_3$, $c_4' = c_4, \ldots, c_k' = c_k$. At this last step, the first quotient becomes 0 while the second quotient is $c_{k+j}'d^{j-1} + c_{k+j-1}'d^{j-2} + \ldots + c_{k+1}'$. Therefore, the second quotient is also zero and, since d is positive, *all* the integers c_{k+j}', $c_{k+j-1}', \ldots, c_{k+1}'$ must be zero. Therefore, the representation is unique.

We now give an example of a number written in a base *larger* than 10. Let us write 275 in the base 12. Since $12^2 < 275 < 12^3$, it can be written in the form $a \cdot 12^2 + b \cdot 12 + c$ where a, b, and c are integers with $0 < a < 12$ and $0 \leq b$, $c < 12$. Using the technique exhibited earlier in this section, we divide 275 by 12, obtaining $275 = 12(22) + 11$; hence $c = 11$. We then divide 22 by 12, obtaining $22 = 12(1) + 10$. Therefore, $b = 10$, $a = 1$, and $275 = 1 \cdot 12^2 + 10 \cdot 12 + 11 = (1\,[10][11])_{12}$. Note that we put brackets about the two-digit coefficients to avoid ambiguity. If we write $(1\ 10\ 11)_{12}$, it could be mistaken for $1 \cdot 12^4 + 1 \cdot 12^3 + 0 \cdot 12^2 + 1 \cdot 12 + 1$. Sometimes symbols are used for the coefficients larger than 9 *provided* the base is not too large. For example, we could use $\alpha = 10$ and $\beta = 11$ in the base 12 and write $275 = (1\ \alpha\ \beta)_{12}$. However, when the base is large, the substitution of symbols becomes very confusing. For instance, in the base 60, we would need 50 distinct symbols for the coefficients between 9 and 60. In such cases, Roman numerals are sometimes used. For example, in the base 60, the number $35 \cdot 60^3 + 25 \cdot 60^2 + 57 \cdot 60 + 55$ can be written as $([35]\ [25]\ [57]\ [55])_{60}$ or $(XXXV\ XXV\ LVII\ LV)_{60}$. As exercises, write 3310 in the base 12 and in the base 60.

In order to impress the student with the importance of number bases, we conclude this section with a few remarks.

There were ancient civilizations that used numbers that were written in the obvious bases of 5 (the fingers on one hand), 10 (the fingers on both hands), and 20 (all the fingers and toes). Other civilizations employed the base 60, probably because 60 had so many divisors that it made it easier to calculate fractions. For this same reason, 12 was also used as a base by some people. There are vestiges of the non-decimal systems everywhere in our present day society. Consider the following examples.

1. The word "score" as in "Fourscore and seven years ago" means 20.

2. The English one pound note is equivalent to 20 shillings.

3. Each hour is divided into 60 minutes, each minute into 60 seconds.

4. One degree in angular measure is divided into 60 minutes, each minute into 60 seconds.

5. One dozen is used for a group of 12 objects, one gross is equivalent to 12 dozens.

6. Twelve inches in a linear foot, twelve hours on a clock dial, twelve months in the year.

Switching to something more up to date, in this century we saw our first electronic computers do their arithmetic in the base 2 using only the digits 0 and 1. A 1 indicated that an electric switch was on, a 0, that it was off. Present-day computers also employ the bases 8 and 16. Ironically, scientists discovered there were backward tribes in Africa and Australia that had not reached the stage of finger counting, but used a primitive type of base 2 arithmetic. It seemed that they counted everything in pairs. They had independent words for the numbers one and two and then they used composite words like two-one for 3, two-two for 4, two-two-one for 5, two-two-two for 6. Beyond 6, they simply used a word that means "many."

Finally, most experts agree that our present-day decimal system was actually invented by the Hindus about 600 A.D. It was transmitted to Europe through the Arabs and became known to European mathematicians about 1200 A.D. However, it was not until approximately 1540 that the new system was in widespread use in Europe. Up to this time, Europeans simply struggled along with the system of Roman numerals.

PROBLEMS

4.1 Write the following decimals in the long form: 4935, 33134, 71268, and 71969.

4.2 Write 278 in the base 3, the base 11, and the base 20.

4.3 Write 5243 in the base 5, the base 7, and the base 2.

4.4 Write 25276 in the base 8, the base 12, and the base 60.

4.5 Express each of the following numbers in the base 2: 6, 28, 496, and 8128.

4.6 Write the decimals 137 and 266 in the long form and then add, multiply, and subtract them in the long form.

4.7 Express 137 and 266 in the base 5 and then add, multiply, and subtract them in the base 5.

4.8 Express 137 and 266 in the base 2 and then add, multiply, and subtract them in the base 2.

4.9 Convert each of the following numbers to the decimal system:
(a) $(1000)_2$ (b) $(1000)_5$
(c) $(10101010111)_2$ (d) $(1234)_5$
(e) $(2136)_7$ (f) $(1\,[11]\,[11]\,[10])_{12}$.

4.10 Find bases x, y, and z such that
(a) $64 = (10)_x$,   (b) $64 = (100)_y$,   (c) $64 = (1000)_z$.

4.11 A gambling casino has red chips worth \$512 each, white chips worth \$64 each, blue chips worth \$8 each, and green chips worth \$1 each. How can it pay each of the following amounts without using more than 7 chips of any one color?
(a) \$678   (b) \$1263   (c) \$2925   (d) \$4012

4.12 (a) In an automobile race, one car completes the race in 3 hours, 8 minutes, and 59 seconds and a second car completes the race in 2 hours, 55 minutes, and 12 seconds. Convert each of the preceding times to seconds. In what base are you working?

(b) In another automobile race, one car finishes the race in 8000 seconds and a second car finishes in 10739 seconds. Convert each of the preceding times to hours, minutes, and seconds.

4.13 Let $x = x_n x_{n-1} \ldots x_3 x_2 x_1$ represent an arbitrary positive integer in the decimal system. Express x in the long form and use Theorems 3.4 and 3.2 to prove each of the following results.

(a) x is divisible by 2 if and only if the integer formed by its *last* digit x_1 is divisible by 2; for example, 27946 is divisible by 2 while 27947 is not (Appendix).

(b) x is divisible by 4 if and only if the integer formed by its last *two* digits $x_2 x_1$ is divisible by 4; for example, 27736 is divisible by 4 while 27946 is not (Appendix).

(c) x is divisible by 8 if and only if the integer formed by its last *three* digits $x_3 x_2 x_1$ is divisible by 8; for example, 27936 is divisible by 8 while 27836 is not.

Would the student care to guess at a criterion for x to be divisible by 16? by 32? Are either of the following integers divisible by 16 or 32: 924012345674832; 123456748396064?

4.14 Let $x = x_n x_{n-1} \ldots x_3 x_2 x_1$ represent an arbitrary integer in the decimal system. Express x in the long form and use Theorems 3.4 and 3.2 to show that x is divisible by 5 if and only if its last digit x_1 is 0 or 5.

4.15 Using the results of Problems 4.13(a) and 4.14, give a criterion for an integer in the decimal system to be divisible by 10.

4.16* Let $x = x_n x_{n-1} \ldots x_3 x_2 x_1$ represent an arbitrary integer in the decimal system. Prove each of the following results.

(a) x is divisible by 9 if and only if the *sum of its digits* $x_n + x_{n-1} + \ldots + x_3 + x_2 + x_1$ is divisible by 9; for example, 12379653 *is* divisible by 9 since the sum of its digits is 36, while 79321535 is *not* divisible by 9 since the sum of its digits is 35. (*Hint.* In each case, express x in the long form and then write 10^k as $(\overset{-k \text{ nines}-}{999\ldots 9} + 1)$ for each $k = 1, 2, 3, \ldots, n - 1$. Distribute the coefficients x_i for $i = 2, \ldots, n$, make a suitable rearrangement of the terms, and then use Theorems 3.4 and 3.2.) (Appendix)

(b) x is divisible by 3 if and only if the *sum of its digits* $x_n + x_{n-1} + \ldots + x_3 + x_2 + x_1$ is divisible by 3; for example, 12376542 *is* divisible by 3 since the sum of its digits is 30, while 19673242 is *not* divisible by 3 since the sum of its digits is 34.

4.17 Use the results of the preceding problem to prove each of the following statements:

(a) If an integer x is divisible by 3, then any rearrangement of its digits produces another integer that is divisible by 3; for example, 381 is divisible by 3 and therefore 318, 813, 831, 138, and 183 are all divisible by 3.

(b) If an integer x is divisible by 9, then any rearrangement of its digits produces another integer that is divisible by 9; for example, 927 is divisible by 9 and therefore 972, 279, 297, 729, and 792 are all divisible by 9.

Section 5

THE GREATEST COMMON DIVISOR

In this section, we discuss the notion of the greatest common divisor of two integers and we present Euclid's Algorithm for finding it. The algorithm is over 2000 years old and it appeared in Book VII of Euclid's *Elements*. The name, Euclid, is so often associated with geometry that we tend to overlook his contributions to the theory of numbers. In fact, three of the thirteen books of Euclid's *Elements* were devoted to number theory. In later sections, we will study other important concepts of number theory that originally appeared in Euclid's *Elements*.

Consider the set of all positive divisors of 12, namely 1, 2, 3, 4, 6, 12 and the set of all positive divisors of 30, namely 1, 2, 3, 5, 6, 10, 15, 30. Now take the set of all *common* divisors, 1, 2, 3, 6; the largest of these is 6. We call 6 the *greatest common divisor* of 12 and 30 and we represent 6 by the symbol $(12, 30)$. In general, for two integers a and b (not both zero), we list all the positive divisors of each and then the common ones. The largest of the common divisors d is called the *greatest common divisor* of a and b and d is represented by the symbol (a, b).

Note that 1 is always a common divisor of any two integers a and b. In cases where 1 is the *greatest* common divisor, we say that a and b are *relatively prime* and we write $(a, b) = 1$. In many cases, it is easy to find the greatest common divisor. For example, the greatest common divisor of 36 and 48 is 12 and we write $(36, 48) = 12$; the greatest common divisor of 32 and 55 is 1 and we write $(32, 55) = 1$. When the numbers are large, however, it may be difficult to find the greatest common divisor. For example, what is the greatest common divisor of 273 and 1066? We will now exhibit a method for finding the greatest common divisor in a special case and then in the general case.

Consider the integers 27 and 48. If we divide 48 by 27, we obtain $48 = 27 \cdot 1 + 21$. Dividing 27 by the remainder 21, we obtain $27 = 21 \cdot 1 + 6$. Now, if we divide 21 by the remainder 6, we have $21 = 6 \cdot 3 + 3$. Finally, dividing 6 by the remainder 3, we obtain $6 = 3 \cdot 2 + 0 = 3 \cdot 2$. The *last nonzero remainder* 3 is the *greatest common divisor* of 27 and 48. Try this technique on 36 and 48 and on 32 and 55, and obtain the answers given earlier. The *general technique is exhibited in the following theorem.*

5.1 Theorem

Euclid's Algorithm for the Greatest Common Divisor

Let a and b be two positive integers with $a > b$. Using the *Division Algorithm*, we divide a by b and obtain integers q_1 and r_1 such that $a = b \cdot q_1 + r_1$ where $0 \le r_1 < b$. Then divide b by r_1, obtaining q_2 and r_2 such that $b = r_1 \cdot q_2 + r_2$ where $0 \le r_2 < r_1$. Continuing, we divide r_1 by r_2, obtaining $r_1 = r_2 \cdot q_3 + r_3$ where $0 \le r_3 < r_2$; dividing r_2 by r_3, we obtain $r_2 = r_3 \cdot q_4 + r_4$ where $0 \le r_4 < r_3$, and so on. In this way, we eventually come to a zero remainder since the remainders $r_1, r_2, r_3, r_4, \ldots$ form a descending sequence of nonnegative integers. Then, the *last nonzero remainder* is the *greatest common divisor* of a and b.

Proof Let us assume, for the sake of brevity and clarity, that in the given process, $r_4 = 0$ and r_3 is the last nonzero remainder. We restate the derived equations reflecting our assumption that $r_4 = 0$,

$$\text{equation 1: } a = b \cdot q_1 + r_1$$
$$\text{equation 2: } b = r_1 \cdot q_2 + r_2$$
$$\text{equation 3: } r_1 = r_2 \cdot q_3 + r_3$$
$$\text{equation 4: } r_2 = r_3 \cdot q_4 + 0.$$

Let us now show that $(a, b) = r_3$. We will first show that r_3 is a *common* divisor of a and b. We will then show that r_3 is divisible by the greatest common divisor of a and b, and that therefore r_3 must be the greatest common divisor. By equation 4, r_3 divides r_2; by equation 3 and Theorem 3.3, r_3 divides r_1; by equation 2 and Theorem 3.3, r_3 divides b; by equation 1 and Theorem 3.3, r_3 divides a. Therefore, r_3 divides a and b, and is a common divisor.

Now, suppose d is the greatest common divisor of a and b. Then d divides a and b, and by equation 1 and Theorem 3.4, d also divides r_1. By equation 2 and Theorem 3.4, d divides r_2; by equation 3 and Theorem 3.4, d finally divides r_3. Consequently $d \le r_3$, however, we have already shown that r_3 is a common divisor of a and b; therefore,

$r_3 \leq d$ since d is the greatest common divisor. Hence, we conclude that $d = r_3$.

As an example, we will now find the greatest common divisor of 273 and 1066 by using Euclid's Algorithm.
Divide 1066 by 273 and we obtain

$$1066 = (273)(3) + 247 .$$

Divide 273 by 247 and we have

$$273 = (247)(1) + 26 .$$

Then divide 247 by 26, obtaining

$$247 = (26)(9) + 13 .$$

Finally, we divide 26 by 13 and obtain a zero remainder. Therefore, 13 is the last nonzero remainder and it is the greatest common divisor of 273 and 1066. Also, observe that $(273, 1066) = (247, 273) = (26, 247) = (13, 26) = 13$. Can you explain this? Can you set up a similar set of equalities for the entries in equations 1, 2, 3, and 4 given in the proof of Euclid's Algorithm?

5.2 Theorem   If $d = (a, b)$, then there exist integers x and y such that $ax + by = d$, i.e., if d is the greatest common divisor of a and b, then d can be written as a *sum of multiples* of a and b.

Proof Consider the first three equations given in the proof of Euclid's Algorithm. Solve each of them for the remainder term, obtaining the following versions of the equations:

$$\text{equation 1: } r_1 = a - bq_1$$
$$\text{equation 2: } r_2 = b - r_1 \cdot q_2$$
$$\text{equation 3: } r_3 = r_1 - r_2 \cdot q_3 .$$

From equation 1, we see that r_1 is expressed as a sum of multiples of a and b. If we substitute this expression for r_1 in equation 2, we obtain r_2 as a sum of multiples of a and b. Finally, substituting for both r_1 and r_2 in equation 3, we obtain r_3 as a sum of multiples of a and b. But in our proof of Euclid's Algorithm, $r_3 = d = (a, b)$. Therefore, we have shown that d can be expressed as a sum of multiples of a and b.

As an example, consider the equations derived in computing the greatest common divisor of 273 and 1066. If we solve each one of them for the remainder term, we have

$$247 = 1066 - (273)(3)$$
$$26 = 273 - 247$$
$$13 = 247 - (26)(9) .$$

In the first equation, 247 is written as a sum of multiples of 1066 and 273. Substituting in the second equation, we obtain

$$26 = 273 - [1066 - (273)(3)] = (1066)(-1) + (273)(4).$$

Hence, 26 is expressed as a sum of multiples of 1066 and 273. Substituting for 26 and 247 in the third equation, we obtain

$$13 = 1066 - (273)(3) - [1066(-1) + (273)(4)](9)$$
$$= (1066)(10) + (273)(-39).$$

Therefore, 13 is expressed as a sum of multiples of 1066 and 273. As an exercise, use the equations given earlier in this section in computing the greatest common divisor of 27 and 48 and express 3 as a sum of multiples of 27 and 48.

5.3 Theorem   (A) If $(a, b) = 1$, then there exist integers x and y such that $ax + by = 1$. (B) If for some integers x and y, we have $ax + by = 1$, then $(a, b) = 1$.

Proof   Part (A) is a special case of the preceding theorem with $d = 1$. Part (B) follows from the fact that $d = (a, b)$ implies that d divides a and b. Therefore, d divides $ax + by$ as well (see Theorem 3.3). But $ax + by = 1$, and so d divides 1 and d must be equal to 1.

As an example, let $a = 97$ and $b = 43$. Then $(97, 43) = 1$ and we will determine integers x and y such that $97x + 43y = 1$. Using Euclid's Algorithm, we obtain

$$97 = (43)(2) + 11$$
$$43 = (11)(3) + 10$$
$$11 = (10)(1) + 1.$$

Solving for the remainders, we obtain

$$11 = 97 - (43)(2)$$
$$10 = 43 - (11)(3)$$
$$1 = 11 - 10.$$

In the first equation, 11 is expressed as a sum of multiples of 97 and 43. Substituting this expression for 11 in the second equation yields

$$10 = 43 - [97 - (43)(2)](3) = (97)(-3) + (43)(7).$$

Substituting for both 10 and 11 in the third equation, we obtain

$$1 = 97 - (43)(2) - [(97)(-3) + (43)(7)] = (97)(4) + (43)(-9).$$

Therefore, 1 is expressed in the form $97x + 43y$ where $x = 4$ and $y = -9$.

5.4 Theorem   Let a, b, and c be positive integers. If a divides the product bc and $(a, b) = 1$, then a divides c.

Proof $(a, b) = 1$ implies (by part (A) of the preceding theorem) that there exist integers x and y such that $ax + by = 1$. Multiplying both sides of this equation by c, we obtain $a(cx) + (bc)y = c$. But a certainly divides $a(cx)$ and since a divides bc, it also divides $(bc)y$. Therefore, a must divide the sum $a(cx) + (bc)y = c$.

Before we state the following corollary, let us recall the definition of a *prime* integer p as an integer greater than 1 that has only 1 and itself as positive divisors.

Corollary Let b and c be positive integers. If a prime integer p divides the product bc, then p divides either b or c.

Proof Let us assume that p does not divide b. We must now show that p divides c. We know that p divides bc, and if p does not divide b, then $(p, b) = 1$ (since p is a prime). Therefore, we simply apply the preceding theorem with $p = a$ and we conclude that p divides c.

Note that the preceding corollary does not hold for integers p that are *not* primes. For example, 6 divides $(2)(9)$ but 6 fails to divide either factor; 12 divides $(4)(15)$ but 12 fails to divide either factor.

PROBLEMS

5.1 Find the greatest common divisor of each of the following pairs of integers:
  (a) 413 and 273 (b) 171 and 133
  (c) 902 and 1034 (d) 1219 and 1643
  (e) 413 and 16278 (f) 7093 and 13489.

5.2 In parts (a), (b), (c), and (d) of the preceding problem, express the greatest common divisor as a *sum of multiples* of the two given integers.

5.3 Show that the following pairs of integers are *relatively prime*, and express 1 as a *sum of multiples* of the two given integers.
  (a) 43 and 57 (b) 69 and 707
  (c) 227 and 1313 (d) 1763 and 1739

5.4 Prove that for any positive integer $n > 1$, the integers $n - 1$ and n are relatively prime.

5.5 (a) Prove that if $(a, b) = 1$, then $(a + b, a - b) = 1$ or 2 (Appendix).
  (b) Suppose both a and b are odd, and $(a, b) = 1$. What can you say about $(a + b, a - b)$?
  (c) Suppose a is odd and b is even, and $(a, b) = 1$. What can you say about $(a + b, a - b)$?
  (d) Find $(127 + 44, 127 - 44)$ and $(127 + 97, 127 - 97)$.

5.6 In Theorem 5.3(B) we saw that if there exist integers x and y such that $ax + by = 1$, then $(a, b) = 1$. Can we generalize this result by showing that if there exist integers x and y such that $ax + by = c$ where c is a positive integer greater than 1, then $(a, b) = c$?

5.7 In each of the following, find integers x and y that satisfy the given equation.

(a) $12x + 5y = 1$

(b) $17x + 19y = 3$ (*Hint.* Determine integers x' and y' such that $17x' + 19y' = 1$, then let $x = 3x'$ and $y = 3y'$.)

5.8 In each of the following, find more than one pair of integers x and y satisfying the given equation.

(a) $12x + 5y = 2$ (b) $15x + 4y = 6$

5.9 Prove that in each of the following, no integers x and y exist that satisfy the given equation.

(a) $12x + 4y = 2$ (b) $5x + 10y = 13$

5.10 As a result of the preceding three problems, can you guess at a condition for the existence of integers x and y satisfying an equation of the form $ax + by = c$ where a, b, and c are positive integers.

Section 6

THE LEAST COMMON MULTIPLE

Let a and b be any two positive integers. If a positive number c is divisible by *both* a and b, it is called a *common multiple* of a and b. Among the common multiples of a and b, there is a smallest one that divides all the other common multiples of a and b and is called the *least common multiple* (l.c.m.) of a and b. It is usually denoted by the symbol $[a, b]$. For example, the set of all positive multiples of 12 consists of 12, 24, 36, 48, 60, 72, 84, 96, 108, 120,..., and the set of all positive multiples of 20 consists of 20, 40, 60, 80, 100, 120,.... The numbers that appear in both of the preceding sets are 60, 120, 180,.... These numbers are the *common* multiples of 12 and 20 and, since 60 is the smallest of these numbers, it is called the *least common multiple* of 12 and 20 and it is represented by the symbol $[12, 20]$. As another example, we list the set of all positive multiples of 5: 5, 10, 15, 20, 25, 30, 35, 40, 45, 50, 55, 60, 65, 70,..., and all the positive multiples of 7: 7, 14, 21, 28, 35, 42, 49, 56, 63, 70,.... The set of all *common* multiples is: 35, 70, 105, 140,... and, since 35 is the smallest of these numbers, it is the *least common multiple* of 5 and 7 and we write $[5, 7] = 35$.

As exercises, find the least common multiple of each of the following pairs of integers: 3 and 5; 6 and 27; 22 and 55; 10 and 33; 24 and 36. Also observe that, in each of the preceding examples and exercises, the least common multiple is always less than or equal to the *product* of the two given integers. Can you explain the reason for this?

In the preceding exercises, it was not difficult to find the least common multiple. However, if the numbers are large, it may be extremely difficult to find the least common multiple without a mechanical method. For example, how would you find the least common multiple of 4199 and 5083? It turns out that the l.c.m. of two positive integers a and b may be obtained by dividing the product ab by the greatest common divisor of a and b. Now we do have a method (Euclid's Algorithm) for finding the g.c.d. of two integers a and b, and so there is a mechanical method available to us. For example, the l.c.m. of 12 and 20 is 60 and $\dfrac{(12)(20)}{4} =$ 60, while the l.c.m. of 5 and 7 is 35 and $\dfrac{5 \cdot 7}{1} = 35$. Verify that this method for finding the l.c.m. works in each of the exercises given earlier in this section. We now state the result in the form of a theorem.

6.1 Theorem

If a and b are any two positive integers, then the *least common multiple* of a and b is equal to the *product* of a and b *divided* by the *greatest common divisor* of a and b, that is, in symbols, $[a, b] = \dfrac{ab}{(a, b)}$.

Proof Let $d = (a, b)$. Then d divides a and d divides b. Hence, there exist integers x and y such that $a = dx$ and $b = dy$ where $(x, y) = 1$. Note that if $(x, y) \neq 1$, then x and y have a common divisor c that must also divide a and b. But then $d \neq (a, b)$, since dc divides a and b and $dc > d$. Now $\dfrac{ab}{d} = \dfrac{(dx)(dy)}{d} = dxy$. Clearly, dxy is a *common* multiple of a and b since $dx = a$ and $dy = b$ are both factors of dxy. To show that dxy is the *least* common multiple of a and b, we must show that dxy *divides* any other common multiple of a and b. Let m be any common multiple of a and b. Then there exist integers z and w such that $m = az$ and $m = bw$. Substituting dx for a and dy for b in each of the preceding equations, we obtain $m = dxz = dyw$. Hence, $xz = yw$ and so y must divide xz; but $(x, y) = 1$ implies that y must divide z (by Theorem 5.4). Therefore, $z = yk$ for some integer k and we may now write $m = dxz = dxyk$. Consequently, dxy is a factor of m where m was *any* common multiple of a and b. Therefore, dxy must be the *least* common multiple of a and b.

Observe that if a and b are any two positive integers, then the product ab is *always* a common multiple of a and b. Also note that, in the special case where a and b are *relatively prime*, the product ab *is* the least common multiple since, by the preceding theorem $[a, b] = \dfrac{ab}{(a, b)} = \dfrac{ab}{1} =$ ab. For example, the l.c.m. of 33 and 100 is 3300 and the l.c.m. of 17 and 20 is 340.

We have now studied the concepts of the g.c.d. and the l.c.m., both of which are over 2000 years old. We shall apply these ideas in many later sections to both old and new problems in number theory and algebra.

PROBLEMS

6.1 Find the l.c.m. of each of the following pairs of integers by using the method described at the very beginning of this section.
(a) 28 and 182   (b)   65 and 85

6.2 In each of the following, use Euclid's Algorithm to find the g.c.d. of the two integers and then find the l.c.m.
(a)   65 and 85   (b)   77 and 221
(c)   28 and 182   (d)   273 and 1066

6.3 Find the l.c.m. of each of the following pairs of integers.
(a)   156 and 228   (b)   97 and 2101
(c)   2233 and 4199 (d)   4199 and 5083

6.4 Find the l.c.m. of each of the following pairs of integers (see Problem 4.16).
(a)   9 and 243081657   (b)   9 and 756910423
(c)   9 and 2976543123

6.5 Prove that if m is the least common multiple of the two integers a and b, every multiple k of a and b is divisible by m. (*Hint*. Divide k by m and show that the remainder is a common multiple of a and b and therefore must be zero.)

Section 7

THE ALGEBRA OF DIVISORS OF AN INTEGER

We shall now introduce you to a finite algebraic system possessing two unusual operations based on the g.c.d. and the l.c.m. of two integers. Even though the concepts of the g.c.d. and the l.c.m. are over 2000 years old, this system is a concrete example of an abstract algebraic system that was invented only within the last 125 years. Examples will be given, and in the exercises and problems that follow, some of the properties of this system will be studied. The student will observe that many of these properties are also valid in the integers under ordinary addition and multiplication, while others are not. Also, some of the properties that hold in the integers are not valid in this new system.

Let S_6 denote the set of all positive divisors of 6, namely 1, 2, 3, and 6. Let the following operations be defined on S_6 : for any two numbers a and b in S_6, $a \circ b = [a, b] = $ l.c.m. of a and b, and $a * b = (a, b) = $ g.c.d. of a and b. The tables that follow give all possible outcomes in S_6 under the $\circ$ and $*$ operations.

L.C.M.		G.C.D.	

$\circ$	1	2	3	6
1	1	2	3	6
2	2	2	6	6
3	3	6	3	6
6	6	6	6	6

$*$	1	2	3	6
1	1	1	1	1
2	1	2	1	2
3	1	1	3	3
6	1	2	3	6

We now give some examples of computations that can be done in S_6 by using the preceding tables. More problems of this type appear in Problem 7.1.

(a) $6 * (1 * 3) = 6 * 1 = 1$

(b) $(2 * 6) \circ (2 * 3) = 2 \circ 1 = 2$

(c) $3 \circ (2 * 6) = 3 \circ 2 = 6$

In general, if we list all the positive divisors of any positive integer n, we will again obtain a finite algebraic system possessing the two operations $\circ$ and $*$. More examples of these systems appear in the problems that follow.

PROBLEMS

7.1 Compute each of the following in S_6 .
  (a) $2 \circ (3 \circ 6)$ (b) $(2 \circ 3) \circ 6$
  (c) $2 * (3 * 6)$ (d) $(2 * 3) * 6$
  (e) $2 \circ (3 * 6)$ (f) $(2 \circ 3) * (2 \circ 6)$
  (g) $3 * (2 \circ 6)$ (h) $(3 * 2) \circ (3 * 6)$

7.2 Construct tables for the $\circ$ and $*$ operations in $S_{10} = \{1, 2, 5, 10\}$. Also, using the tables, compute each of the following in S_{10} .
  (a) $5 * (5 \circ 2)$ (b) $(5 * 2) \circ (5 * 10)$
  (c) $5 \circ (2 \circ 10)$ (d) $(5 \circ 2) * (5 \circ 10)$

7.3 Construct tables for the $\circ$ and $*$ operations in $S_{12} = \{1, 2, 3, 4, 6, 12\}$. Also, using the tables, compute each of the following in S_{12} .
  (a) $4 \circ (6 * 12)$ (b) $(4 \circ 6) * (4 \circ 12)$
  (c) $3 * (4 \circ 6)$ (d) $(3 * 4) \circ (3 * 6)$

7.4 Construct tables for the $\circ$ and $*$ operations in

$$S_{30} = \{1, 2, 3, 5, 6, 10, 15, 30\} .$$

Also, using the tables, compute each of the following in S_{30} .
  (a) $5 \circ (15 * 30)$ (b) $(5 \circ 15) * (5 \circ 30)$
  (c) $10 * (5 \circ 15)$ (d) $(10 * 5) \circ (10 * 15)$

7.5 (a) Find S_{29} and construct tables for the $\circ$ and $*$ operations.
  (b) Find S_{47} and construct tables for the $\circ$ and $*$ operations.
  (c) Find S_p where p is any prime and construct tables for the $\circ$ and $*$ operations.

7.6 (a) Find S_{21} and construct tables for the $\circ$ and $*$ operations.
  (b) Find S_{35} and construct tables for the $\circ$ and $*$ operations.
  (c) Find S_{pq} where p and q are distinct primes and construct tables for the $\circ$ and $*$ operations.

7.7 Determine which of the following properties are satisfied by the $\circ$ and $*$ operations on S_6, S_{10}, S_{12}, and S_{30} . Which of the properties are satisfied in S_n for any positive integer n?

(a) Closure

(b) Commutative Law

(c) Associative Law

(d) Identity

(e) Cancellation Law

(f) Distributive Law for ∘ with respect to *

(g) Distributive Law for * with respect to ∘

(h) $a \circ a = a$ for every element a

(i) $a * a = a$ for every element a

7.8 Compare the properties mentioned in the preceding problem in relation to S_n with the corresponding properties for the integers under ordinary addition and multiplication. Which properties are satisfied in both systems?

Section 8

PRIME INTEGERS

In this section, we discuss some very important properties of prime integers and their applications to problems in number theory. We first exhibit a systematic method for finding primes, called the *sieve* method. It was discovered by the Greek mathematician and astronomer, Eratosthenes, about 225 B.C. Variations of this method have been used over the past twenty years on electronic computers to construct large tables of primes. We then prove that there are infinitely many primes using a proof that is essentially the same as the one that appeared in Book IX of Euclid's *Elements* about 300 B.C. We conclude this section with a discussion of the factorization of integers into a product of primes. The essential idea of prime factorization was also contained in Book IX of Euclid's *Elements*, although many of its more important applications came much later.

An integer $p > 1$ is called a *prime* if its only positive divisors are 1 and p. If an integer $n > 1$ has at least one positive divisor other than itself and 1, we call n a *composite* integer. For example, 2, 3, 5, 7, 11, 13, and 17 are primes while 4, 6, 8, 9, 10, 12, 14, 15, and 16 are composite integers.

8.1 Theorem A composite integer n is always divisible by a prime $p \leq \sqrt{n}$.

Proof If n is composite, it has divisors other than 1 and itself. Consider the set of all divisors d of n such that $1 < d < n$. By the Well-

Ordering Axiom, this set has a least integer p which *must* be a prime. If p is not a prime, then p is composite and $p = ab$ where $1 < a < p$. But p divides n and therefore a must also divide n. This is not possible since $a < p$ and p was the least integer in the set in all divisors d of n with $1 < d < n$. Therefore, we have found a prime p which divides n and thus $n = pc$ for some integer $c \geq p$ (since c is a divisor of n and p is the least divisor of n). Consequently, we have the following relations:

$$p^2 = p \cdot p \leq p \cdot c = n.$$

Therefore, $p^2 \leq n$ and $p \leq \sqrt{n}$. We have now proved that the least divisor p of n is less than the square root of n.

THE SIEVE METHOD

As a result of the preceding theorem, we can state that if an integer $n > 1$ is *not* divisible by a prime $p \leq \sqrt{n}$, then n *must* be a prime. This gives rise to a method of listing all primes up to a given number n. We call this method the *sieve* method and we illustrate it by finding all primes less than 81.

Since 2 is the only even prime, we know that no even integer greater than 2 can be a prime. Hence, we start with 2 and a list of all *odd* integers between 1 and 81.

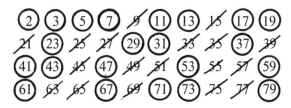

The square root of 81 is 9 and the only primes less than 9 are 2, 3, 5, and 7. We circled these on the preceding list. Now, any integer less than 81 which is *not* divisible by 2, 3, 5, or 7 must be a prime by the preceding theorem. Therefore, we systematically delete from our list all multiples of 3 greater than 3, all multiples of 5 greater than 5, and all multiples of 7 greater than 7. Note that we have already eliminated all multiples of 2 greater than 2 by simply *not* writing the *even* integers between 2 and 81. The numbers that remain on the list are then circled, and these are all the primes less than 81. As an exercise, use the sieve method to list all the primes less than 121. How many primes would be needed to construct a table of all primes <900?

HOW MANY PRIMES ARE THERE?

It is clear that there is no last positive integer, i.e., there are infinitely many positive integers. If k were the last one, $k + 1$ would be another, and so k could not be the last one. There are also infinitely many even integers, for if $2k$ were the last one, then $2k + 2$ would be another, and thus $2k$ could not be the last even integer. Similarly, there can be no last odd integer $2k + 1$, since $2k + 3$ would be another one larger than $2k + 1$. When we come to the primes, however, it is not quite that simple to show that there is no last prime. For if k is the last prime, we cannot say that $k + 1$ is a larger prime since $k + 1$ is always even for any prime $k > 2$. In fact, we cannot add any fixed number to a prime and be certain of getting another prime. Therefore, we need a different type of argument to establish that there is no last prime. We give this argument in the following theorem.

8.2 Theorem   There are infinitely many primes.

Proof Suppose there are *not* infinitely many primes. Then there is a last prime; let us call it Q. We may now list *all* the primes: 2, 3, 5, 7, 11, . . . , Q. Form a new integer by taking the product of all the primes on the preceding list. Then add 1 to this product and obtain an integer N where $N = (2 \cdot 3 \cdot 5 \cdot 7 \cdot 11 \cdots Q) + 1$. It is clear that N is composite since $N > Q$ and Q is the last prime. By Theorem 8.1, N must be divisible by a prime $p \leq \sqrt{N}$. Therefore, p must be on the list of primes 2, 3, 5, 7, 11, . . . , Q. But this is not possible since each prime on the list, upon division by N, leaves a remainder of 1. Consequently, we have found another prime p that is *not* on the given list of primes, and thus we did not have a list of *all* the primes in the first place. Therefore, there is no last prime, and hence there are infinitely many.

As examples of the construction of the integer N and its use in the proof, find a prime divisor of each of the following integers:

$$2 \cdot 3 \cdot 5 \cdot 7 + 1 = 211$$
$$2 \cdot 3 \cdot 5 \cdot 7 \cdot 11 + 1 = 2311$$
$$2 \cdot 3 \cdot 5 \cdot 7 \cdot 11 \cdot 13 + 1 = 30031$$
$$2 \cdot 3 \cdot 5 \cdot 7 \cdot 11 \cdot 13 \cdot 17 + 1 = 510511$$

PRIME FACTORIZATION

8.3 Theorem

The Fundamental Theorem of Arithmetic

Every composite integer n can be factored into a product of primes in a unique way, except perhaps for the order of the factors.

Before the proof, we give some examples. We may factor 24 into a product of primes in any of the following ways: $2 \cdot 2 \cdot 2 \cdot 3$, $2 \cdot 3 \cdot 2 \cdot 2, 3 \cdot 2 \cdot 2 \cdot 2, 2 \cdot 2 \cdot 3 \cdot 2$. We may factor 36 into a product of primes in any of the following ways: $2 \cdot 3 \cdot 2 \cdot 3, 2 \cdot 3 \cdot 3 \cdot 2$, $2 \cdot 2 \cdot 3 \cdot 3, 3 \cdot 3 \cdot 2 \cdot 2, 3 \cdot 2 \cdot 3 \cdot 2, 3 \cdot 2 \cdot 2 \cdot 3$. We may factor 51 as $3 \cdot 17$ or $17 \cdot 3$. Note that if we write the prime factors in such a way that the factors are *nondecreasing*, then we obtain only the following prime factorizations: $24 = 2 \cdot 2 \cdot 2 \cdot 3$; $36 = 2 \cdot 2 \cdot 3 \cdot 3$; $51 = 3 \cdot 17$. In fact, if we combine equal primes under a single exponent, we obtain the following factorizations: $24 = 2^3 \cdot 3$; $36 = 2^2 \cdot 3^2$; $51 = 3 \cdot 17$. This *last* factorization is called the *canonical* or *standard* factorization of each of the integers.

Now, we call *any* factorization of an integer into a product of primes a *prime factorization* of the integer. However, the factorization that combines *equal* primes under a *single* exponent with the *unequal* primes written in *ascending* order is the *only* one that is called the *canonical* or *standard* factorization of the integer.

As further examples of the canonical factorization, we have $30 = 2 \cdot 3 \cdot 5$; $300 = 2^2 \cdot 3 \cdot 5^2$; $360 = 2^3 \cdot 3^2 \cdot 5$; $8820 = 2^2 \cdot 3^2 \cdot 5 \cdot 7^2$; $207900 = 2^2 \cdot 3^3 \cdot 5^2 \cdot 7 \cdot 11$.

Proof of Theorem 8.3 Let n be any composite integer. By Theorem 8.1, n is divisible by a prime $p_1 \leq \sqrt{n}$. Therefore, $n = p_1 \cdot a_1$. If a_1 is a prime, we are finished, since n equals a product of primes. If a_1 is composite, it must also be divisible by a prime $p_2 \leq \sqrt{a_1}$. Then $a_1 = p_2 \cdot a_2$ and $n = p_1 \cdot p_2 \cdot a_2$. If a_2 is a prime, we are done. If a_2 is composite, it has a prime divisor p_3. Then $a_2 = p_3 \cdot a_3$ and $n = p_1 \cdot p_2 \cdot p_3 \cdot a_3$. Continuing this process, we obtain a *nonincreasing* sequence of positive integers $a_1, a_2, a_3, \ldots, a_k$ until we eventually come to a prime a_k. Then $n = p_1 \cdot p_2 \cdot p_3 \cdots p_k \cdot a_k$ is a prime factorization of n.

To prove the uniqueness of such a factorization (except for the order of the factors), suppose there exists a composite number n with two prime factorizations. Then $n = p_1 \cdot p_2 \cdot p_3 \cdots p_r = q_1 \cdot q_2 \cdot q_3 \cdots q_k$ where $r \leq k$. Now p_1 divides n, and so p_1 divides the product $q_1 \cdot q_2 \cdot q_3 \cdots q_k$. By the Corollary to Theorem 5.4, p_1 must divide one of the factors $q_1, q_2, q_3, \ldots$, or q_k. Suppose p_1 divides q_1; then, since p_1 and q_1 are both primes, $p_1 = q_1$ and we may cancel them, obtaining the integer $n/p_1 = p_2 \cdot p_3 \cdots p_r = q_2 \cdot q_3 \cdots q_k$. But p_2 divides n/p_1 and must divide the product $q_2 \cdot q_3 \cdots q_k$. Applying the Corollary to Theorem 5.4, we find that p_2 divides one of the factors of the product $q_2 \cdot q_3 \cdots q_k$. Suppose p_2 divides the factor q_2. Then $p_2 = q_2$ and we cancel p_2 and q_2, obtaining $n/(p_1 \cdot p_2) = p_3 \cdot p_4 \cdots p_r = q_3 \cdot q_4 \cdots q_k$. Continuing this process, we obtain $p_3 = q_3, p_4 = q_4, \ldots, p_r = q_r$ and we finally arrive at $n/(p_1 \cdot p_2 \cdot p_3 \cdots p_r) = 1 = q_{r+1} \cdot q_{r+2} \cdots q_k$. Consequently, each of the factors $q_{r+1}, q_{r+2}, \ldots, q_k$ must be 1. But this is not possible since the factors $q_{r+1}, q_{r+2}, \ldots, q_k$ are supposed to be primes. Hence, $r = k$ and the factorizations $p_1 \cdot p_2 \cdot p_3 \cdots p_r$ and $q_1 \cdot q_2 \cdot q_3 \cdots q_r$ are the same.

As a further example, we now find the canonical or standard factorization of the integer 66340. First we deal with the obvious factor of 10, arriving at

$$66340 = (6634)(10) \, .$$

But 6634 is divisible by 2, so we obtain $6634 = 2(3317)$ and $66340 = 2 \cdot 10 \cdot 3317 = 2^2 \cdot 5 \cdot 3317$. Now $3317 < (59)^2$, so $\sqrt{3317} < 59$. To determine whether there are prime factors of 3317, we must divide 3317 by each prime < 59 (by Theorem 8.1). It turns out that 31 divides 3317 and the standard factorization of $66340 = 2^2 \cdot 5 \cdot 31 \cdot 107$. The student should verify that 107 is a prime by dividing it by 2, 3, 5, and 7 and showing that none of them divides it.

The preceding theorem on unique prime factorization is one of the most important theorems in all of mathematics. It opens the door to future discussions of interesting problems in number theory. Many important applications of the Fundamental Theorem of Arithmetic will come up in the next four sections. The student should remember that the *uniqueness* of the factorization into primes is a key part of the theorem. There are examples of number systems in which there is a factorization into primes but in which the factorization is *not* unique (see Problem 8.14 at the end of this section).

PROBLEMS

8.1 Find the standard factorization of each of the following integers.
   (a) 496   (b) 1003
   (c) 1009   (d) 5184
   (e) 5521   (f) 8128
   (g) 10403   (h) 65536
   (i) 162440   (j) 171500
   (k) 262144   (l) 373248

8.2 Does the expression $x^2 - x + 41$ yield a prime for $x = 1, 2, 3, 4, 5,$ and 6? Will this expression yield a prime for every positive integer x?

8.3* If p is a prime, will the integer $2^p - 1$ always be a prime?

8.4 In this problem, we use the symbol $n!$ for the product $n(n-1)(n-2) \cdots (3)(2)(1)$ where n is any positive integer. For example, $3! = 3 \cdot 2 \cdot 1$, $5! = 5 \cdot 4 \cdot 3 \cdot 2 \cdot 1$, $10! = 10 \cdot 9 \cdot 8 \cdot 7 \cdot 6 \cdot 5 \cdot 4 \cdot 3 \cdot 2 \cdot 1$. Also note that $1! = 1$ whereas $0!$ is *defined* to be 1.

In each of the following, determine all values of the positive integer n for which the given expression is a *prime*.
   (a) $n! + 7$
   (b) $n! + 12$
   (c) $n! + 25$

8.5 In this problem, we also use the factorial symbol as defined in the preceding problem.

In what follows, determine all values of the positive integer $n \leq 10$ for which the given expression is a *composite* number.

  (a) $3! + n$
  (b) $5! + n$
  (c) $10! + n$

8.6 (a)   Find a set of 5 consecutive composite integers.
  (b)   Find a set of 7 consecutive composite integers.
  (c)   Find a set of at least 10 consecutive composite integers.
  (d)* Prove that you can always find a set of at least n consecutive composite integers for any positive integer n.

8.7 If for an odd prime p, we have $p + 2$ is also a prime, then p and $p + 2$ are called *twin primes*. For example, we have 3 and 5, 17 and 19, and 41 and 43. There are many other examples of *twin primes*, and among the larger known ones are $1,000,000,000,061$ and $1,000,000,000,063$.
  Answer each of the following questions.

  (a)   Find the first 10 examples of *twin primes*.
  (b)   Prove that if one is added to a product of *twin primes*, a perfect square is always obtained. Find the value of this perfect square. Does this result depend on the fact that we are dealing with *twin primes*?
  (c)   Only a finite number of examples of *twin primes* are known, yet many mathematicians suspect that infinitely many exist. This would mean that no matter how far we go out in the system of positive integers, there will be consecutive primes separated by only one composite integer. However, the result in Problem 8.6(d) seems to indicate that for large n, we can separate consecutive primes by at least n composite integers. Thus, it seems on one hand that we can separate consecutive primes by arbitrarily long sequences of consecutive composite integers, while on the other hand there are examples of twin primes that are separated by the minimum number of composite numbers, namely one. Is there anything contradictory in these statements? Explain your answer.

8.8 (a)   Find five primes of the form $3k + 2$ when k is a positive integer.
  (b)   Show that there exist infinitely many primes of the type $3k + 2$. (*Hint.* By the Division Algorithm, every integer n has one of the forms $3k$, $3k + 1$, $3k + 2$. Since the first form $3k$ is a multiple of 3, it can never yield a prime for $k > 1$. Therefore, only the latter two forms can yield a prime. Assume (as in Theorem 8.2) that there are finitely many primes of the type $3k + 2$. Then list them as $P_1, P_2, P_3, \ldots, P_r$ and form the integer $N = 3(P_1 \cdot P_2 \ldots P_r) + 2$.) (Appendix)

8.9 (a)   Find five primes of the form $4k + 3$ where k is a positive integer.
  (b)* Show that there exist infinitely many primes of the type $4k + 3$.

8.10 (a)   Find five primes of the form $6k + 1$ where k is a positive integer.
  (b)   Find five primes of the form $6k + 5$ where k is a positive integer.
  (c)   Prove that every prime greater than 5 is of the form $6k + 1$ or $6k + 5$ where k is a positive integer.
  (d)* Prove that there are infinitely many primes of the form $6k + 5$ where k is a positive integer.

8.11 Two conjectures were made by the eighteenth century mathematician Christian Goldbach. To date, neither one has been shown to be true

PRIME INTEGERS   39

or false. However, most experts feel that they are both true. In fact, the first conjecture has been verified for all even numbers up to 33,000,000. We now state the conjectures with some examples, and we ask some questions relating to them.

1. Every *even number* greater than 4 can be written as the sum of *two odd primes*.

As examples,

$$6 = 3 + 3$$
$$12 = 5 + 7$$
$$20 = 3 + 17 = 7 + 13$$
$$32 = 3 + 29 = 13 + 19$$
$$50 = 3 + 47 = 7 + 43 = 13 + 37 = 19 + 31$$

2. Every *odd number* greater than 7 can be written as the sum of *three odd primes*.

As examples,

$$9 = 3 + 3 + 3$$
$$13 = 3 + 3 + 7$$
$$15 = 3 + 5 + 7$$
$$19 = 3 + 3 + 13 = 3 + 5 + 11 = 5 + 7 + 7$$
$$23 = 3 + 3 + 17 = 3 + 7 + 13 = 5 + 5 + 13 = 5 + 7 + 11$$

(a) Write each of the following numbers as the sum of two odd primes in as many ways as possible: 30, 40, 48, 102, and 120.

(b) Write each of the following numbers as the sum of three odd primes in as many ways as possible: 27, 31, and 63.

(c) Prove that if conjecture 1 is true, then conjecture 2 must be true.

(d) Does the truth of conjecture 2 imply the truth of conjecture 1?

8.12 (a) 496 has 10 positive divisors including 1 and itself. Begin with the standard factorization of 496 and find the standard factorization of each of the remaining divisors.

(b) 360 has 24 positive divisors including 1 and itself. Begin with the standard factorization of 360 and find the standard factorization of each of the remaining divisors.

8.13 (a) Using Euclid's Algorithm, find the g.c.d. and the l.c.m. of 4500 and 600. Then find the standard factorizations of all four numbers and compare them.

(b) Using Euclid's Algorithm, find the g.c.d. and the l.c.m. of 504 and 540. Then find the standard factorizations of all four numbers and compare them.

8.14 Let E be the set of all positive even integers. E is certainly closed under multiplication (see Problem 3.5). We now define what we mean by a prime in E. We use the term E-prime to distinguish the primes in E from our regular prime integers.

Definition

An E-prime is any positive even integer that *cannot* be factored into a product of two smaller even integers.

As examples, 2, 6, 10, 14, and 18 are E-primes, and, in fact, any positive integer that is 2 times an odd integer is an E-prime. Hence, there are infinitely many *E*-primes. As examples of composite numbers in *E*, consider 4, 8, 12, 16, and 20.

Answer each of the following questions.

(a) Are there any *E*-primes that are *not* of the form $2k$ where k is a positive odd integer?

(b) List the first ten *E*-primes.

(c) Factor each of the following numbers into a product of *E*-primes: 16, 20, 30, 36, 40, 50, 60, and 140.

(d) Show that every even integer is either an *E*-prime or can be factored into a product of *E*-primes.

(e) Show that the factorization of an even integer into a product of *E*-primes is *not* unique by exhibiting more than one factorization of each of the following integers into *E*-primes: 16, 36, 40, 60, and 140.

Section 9

THE NUMBER OF DIVISORS OF AN INTEGER

We deal here with a method for computing the *number* of positive divisors of an integer n including 1 and n itself. If n is small, there is little difficulty in listing all the divisors and then counting them. However, when n is large and has many divisors, it becomes somewhat of a problem. For example, how long would it take to list and count all the divisors of 360, or even all the divisors of 60? It is clear that for a large number possessing an abundance of divisors, a *systematic* way is needed in order to count the total number of positive divisors.

We begin with some fairly simple observations. If an integer p is a prime, it has exactly *two* positive divisors 1 and p, while the number p^2 has precisely *three* positive divisors 1, p, and p^2. In fact, it is not difficult to see that if p is any prime and i is any positive integer, the number p^i has exactly $i + 1$ divisors; these are $1, p, p^2, p^3, \ldots, p^i$. Hence, the number of divisors of p^i is *one more than* the exponent i. For example, 7^4 has 5 divisors: $1, 7, 7^2, 7^3$, and 7^4; and 5^6 has 7 divisors: $1, 5, 5^2, 5^3$, $5^4, 5^5$, and 5^6.

Now suppose the standard factorization of a number a has the form $p^i q^j$. How many positive divisors does a have? Once again, it is not difficult to see that a systematic listing of all the positive divisors of a yields $(i + 1)(j + 1)$ divisors. Note that this is a product of *one more than* the exponent i with *one more than* the exponent j. Thus we actually obtain the number of positive divisors of a by taking the product of the *number* of divisors that each prime power has in the standard factorization of a. The reason for this is that each divisor of a must be a product of one of the $i + 1$ divisors of p^i with one of the $j + 1$ divisors of q^j, and there are precisely $(i + 1)(j + 1)$ ways to form such products. For example, $12 = 2^2 \cdot 3$ has $3 \times 2 = 6$ divisors, and we obtain them by putting each of the 3 divisors of 2^2 with each of the 2 divisors of 3. The divisors of 12 are

$$
\begin{array}{ccc}
1 & 2 & 2^2 \\
3 & 2 \cdot 3 & 2^2 \cdot 3
\end{array}
$$

As exercises, list the 12 divisors of $108 = 2^2 \cdot 3^3$ and the 20 divisors of $432 = 2^4 \cdot 3^3$.

Now if we proceed to a number b that has a canonical factorization of the form $p^i q^j r^k$, it is not difficult to conclude that each divisor of b is a product consisting of one of the $i + 1$ divisors of p^i, one of the $j + 1$ divisors of q^j and one of the $k + 1$ divisors of r^k. But there are exactly $(i + 1)(j + 1)(k + 1)$ ways of forming such products. Therefore b has exactly $(i + 1)(j + 1)(k + 1)$ positive divisors. Once again, note that this product is formed by taking *one more than* each exponent and then multiplying these numbers together. For example, $60 = 2^2 \cdot 3 \cdot 5$ has $3 \times 2 \times 2 = 12$ divisors, and we obtain them by forming all possible products using one of the 3 divisors of 2^2, one of the 2 divisors of 3, and one of the 2 divisors of 5. The divisors of 60 are

$$
\begin{array}{ccc}
1 & 2 & 2^2 \\
3 & 2 \cdot 3 & 2^2 \cdot 3 \\
5 & 2 \cdot 5 & 2^2 \cdot 5 \\
3 \cdot 5 & 2 \cdot 3 \cdot 5 & 2^2 \cdot 3 \cdot 5
\end{array}
$$

As exercises, list the 18 divisors of $180 = 2^2 \cdot 3^2 \cdot 5$ and the 24 divisors of $360 = 2^3 \cdot 3^2 \cdot 5$.

Finally, we state without a formal proof, a theorem, in which the *general* technique for determining the number of divisors of an integer is given.

9.1 Theorem

Let n be any positive integer greater than 1. The number of positive divisors of n may be obtained in the following manner.

1. Find the standard factorization of n.
2. Add 1 to each of the exponents that appear in the standard factorization.
3. Take the product of all the increased exponents.

As an example, we find the number of positive divisors of 12600.

1. The standard factorization of 12600 is $2^3 \cdot 3^2 \cdot 5^2 \cdot 7$.
2. The exponents are 3, 2, 2, and 1; adding 1 to each exponent, we obtain the increased exponents 4, 3, 3, and 2.

3. Form the product $4 \cdot 3 \cdot 3 \cdot 2 = 72$. Hence, there are 72 positive divisors of 12600.

In closing this discussion, let us make it clear that the technique works *only* with the exponents in the *standard* or *canonical* factorization of the integer n. For example, $12 = 2^2 \cdot 3$ and we obtain $3 \times 2 = 6$ divisors. However, if we take the product of the increased exponents in any of the following factorizations, we arrive at wrong answers: $4 \cdot 3$; $2 \cdot 6$; $2 \cdot 2 \cdot 3$. Note, in particular, that even the prime factorization $2 \cdot 2 \cdot 3$ yields the wrong answer, since it is *not* in the *standard* form.

PROBLEMS

9.1 Find the *number* of positive divisors of each of the following integers:
(a) 496
(b) 2311
(c) 3600
(d) 8128
(e) 8820
(f) 207900

9.2 List all the positive divisors of 496 and 8128.

9.3 In each of the following, find the smallest positive integer that has precisely the given number of positive divisors.
(a) 7 divisors (Appendix)
(b) 6 divisors (Appendix)
(c) 8 divisors
(d) 97 divisors

9.4 Suppose we denote by $(n)^*$ the number of positive divisors of the positive integer n. For example, $(6)^* = 4, (9)^* = 3, (60)^* = 12$, and $(360)^* = 24$. Compute
(a) $(100)^*$ (b) $(160)^*$ (c) $(1250)^*$

9.5 (a) Compute $((12)(45))^*$ and show that it is *less* than $(12)^* \cdot (45)^*$.
(b) Find two other numbers a and b such that $(ab)^*$ is less than $(a)^* \cdot (b)^*$.

9.6 (a) Show that $((40)(63))^* = (40)^* \cdot (63)^*$.
(b) Show that $((36)(275))^* = (36)^* \cdot (275)^*$.
(c) Find two other numbers a and b such that $(ab)^* = (a)^* \cdot (b)^*$.
(d) Prove that if a and b are *relatively prime*, then $(ab)^* = (a)^* \cdot (b)^*$.
(e) Is the converse of the statement in (d) true?

9.7 Find the number of divisors of each of the following products.
(a) $(97)(2311)$
(b) $(97)(1649)$
(c) $(63)(5500)$
(d) $(188)(1107)$

9.8* Show that $(ab)^* \le (a)^* \cdot (b)^*$ for any positive integers a and b greater than 1 (Appendix).

THE G.C.D., L.C.M., AND PRIME FACTORIZATION

We now apply prime factorization to the problem of finding the g.c.d. and the l.c.m. of two integers a and b. We have already discussed these concepts in Sections 5 and 6, and a method that employed Euclid's Algorithm was given for the solution of problems dealing with the g.c.d. and the l.c.m. In this section, we seek a new approach to this problem and we obtain a solution by using the standard factorization of the integers a and b. However, it is not always possible to apply the prime factorization technique in specific problems where the standard factorizations of a and b are difficult to find. For example, suppose $a = 19511$ and $b = 168367$. How would you find the standard factorizations of a and b? It turns out that $a = (109)(179)$ and $b = (101)(1667)$; therefore, $(a, b) = 1$. In this example, finding the standard factorizations would have been extremely difficult. Consequently, in cases where the numbers a and b cannot be factored easily, the student must continue to use Euclid's Algorithm. It is still the only sure way to find the g.c.d. In the preceding example, using Euclid's Algorithm on 19511 and 168367, we eventually arrive at a remainder of 1. Thus, we conclude that a and b are relatively prime *without* ever finding the standard factorizations.

We shall now explain how to find the g.c.d. and the l.c.m. by a new method based on the standard factorization of an integer. This method can be used in a variety of problems yielding fairly quick solutions with the added bonus that the g.c.d. and the l.c.m. are obtained in factored form.

We begin with a simple example. Suppose $a = 2^3 \cdot 3^3 \cdot 7$ and $b = 2^2 \cdot 3^4 \cdot 7^2$. To form the g.c.d. of a and b, we require the *largest* number that divides both a and b. In comparing exponents, we see that 2^2 is the highest power of 2 to divide a and b, 3^3 is the highest power of 3 that divides a and b, and 7 is the highest power of 7 to divide a and b. Therefore, $(a, b) = 2^2 \cdot 3^3 \cdot 7$. Observe that in forming the g.c.d., we ended up choosing the *smaller* exponent of each of the primes *common* to the standard factorizations of a and b.

On the other hand, to form the l.c.m. of a and b, we require the *smallest* number that can be divided by *both* a and b. Therefore, the l.c.m. of a and b must have a factor of 2^3 to accommodate a, a factor of 3^4 to accommodate b, and a factor of 7^2 to accommodate b. Therefore, $[a, b] = 2^3 \cdot 3^4 \cdot 7^2$. Notice that in obtaining the l.c.m., we ended up selecting the *larger* exponent of each of the primes *common* to the standard factorizations of a and b.

Now suppose $a = 2^3 \cdot 3^2 \cdot 7^2 \cdot 13$ and $b = 2^2 \cdot 3^3 \cdot 5^2 \cdot 11^3$. At this point, for the sake of convenience, we introduce some new terminology. Whenever a prime appears *only* in the factorization of *one* of the numbers a or b, we call it an *uncommon* prime. The *uncommon* primes in the preceding factorizations of a and b are 5, 7, 11, and 13. To construct the g.c.d. of a and b, we need the largest number that divides *both* a and b. In comparing exponents of the primes that are *common* to the standard factorizations of a and b, we see that 2^2 is the highest power of 2 to divide both a and b, and 3^2 is the highest power of 3 that divides both a and b. Clearly, the *uncommon* primes 5, 7, 11, and 13 cannot appear in the factorization of the g.c.d. of a and b, since none of them divides *both* a and b. Therefore, $(a, b) = 2^2 \cdot 3^2$. Observe that in forming the g.c.d. of a and b, we again selected the *smaller* exponent of each of the primes that were *common* to the factorizations of a and b and we ignored the *uncommon* primes.

To construct the l.c.m. of a and b, we require the smallest number that can be divided by *both* a and b. Hence, it must have among its factors every *uncommon* prime to whatever power it is raised in the factorization of a or b. However, in looking for the prime factors of the l.c.m. that are *common* to the factorizations of a and b, we need only select those primes with the *larger* exponents, since these will accommodate the common primes to whatever power they are raised in the factorizations of a and b. Joining these to the *uncommon* primes, we obtain $[a, b] = 2^3 \cdot 3^3 \cdot 5^2 \cdot 7^2 \cdot 11^3 \cdot 13$.

The general technique is valuable since it does give quick results *provided* the standard factorizations of a and b are known. We shall now state, without a formal proof, a theorem in which we give the *general* technique for determining the g.c.d. and the l.c.m. of two integers a and b by the method of standard factorization.

Let a and b be two positive integers greater than 1. The g.c.d. and the l.c.m. of a and b may be obtained in the following way.

1. Find the *standard factorization* of a and b.
2. Note the *uncommon* primes.
3. Note the *common* primes and compare exponents.
4. For the g.c.d., take the product of the *common* primes, choosing the *smaller* of the exponents in each case.
5. For the l.c.m., take the product of *all* the *uncommon* primes to whatever power they are raised in the factorization of either a or b, together with the product of the *common* primes, choosing the *larger* of the exponents in each case.

As another example, we find the g.c.d. and the l.c.m. of $a = 1008$ and $b = 2700$ using the general technique.

1. $1008 = 2^4 \cdot 3^2 \cdot 7$ and $2700 = 2^2 \cdot 3^3 \cdot 5^2$.
2. The *uncommon* primes are 5 and 7.
3. The common primes are 2 and 3.
4. $(1008, 2700) = 2^2 \cdot 3^2$.
5. $[1008, 2700] = 2^4 \cdot 3^3 \cdot 5^2 \cdot 7$.

As a final exercise, find the g.c.d. of 1008 and 2700 by using Euclid's Algorithm, and compare the two methods of solution.

PROBLEMS

10.1 Find the standard factorization of the g.c.d. and the l.c.m. of a and b where

$$a = 2^5 \cdot 3^3 \cdot 7^2 \cdot 13^3 \cdot 19^2 \cdot 23^4 \cdot 29^3$$
$$b = 2^3 \cdot 3^4 \cdot 5^2 \cdot 11^2 \cdot 13^4 \cdot 19 \cdot 23^2 \cdot 31$$

10.2 Using the *prime factorization* technique, find the g.c.d. and the l.c.m. of each of the following pairs of integers.
(a) 360 and 2700
(b) 6368 and 7623
(c) 11011 and 45815
(d) 6368 and 11011

10.3 By using *prime factorization*, find the g.c.d. and the l.c.m. of each of the following pairs of integers. Check your answer for the g.c.d. by using Euclid's Algorithm.
(a) 2233 and 4199
(b) 4199 and 5083

    (c)   1219 and 1643
    (d)   413 and 16278
    (e)   7093 and 13489

10.4   Using prime factorization, prove that if $(a, b) = 1$, then $[a, b] = ab$.

10.5* Using prime factorization, prove Theorem 6.1 (Appendix).

A DIFFERENT TYPE OF FACTORIZATION

We come now to a very recent application of the standard prime factorization of an integer. Much of this material became generally known in the early 1960's and research is continuing on many unsolved problems connected with it. Unfortunately, since the topic is so new, mathematicians have not yet had time to find very many practical applications of it. However, in the future there may be important concrete applications of this material. For the present, we introduce the student to the subject for the simple reason that it applies and extends the notion of the standard factorization of an integer.

We know from the Fundamental Theorem of Arithmetic that every integer can be factored uniquely into a product of powers of primes. Now suppose we take each exponent in the standard factorization of an integer and factor it into its standard factorization. We then have a *new* form of the prime factorization of the integer. Now, if we again factor each remaining non-prime exponent into its standard factorization, we obtain yet another *new* form of the prime factorization of the same integer. If we continue this process of factoring the remaining non-prime exponents until every number that appears in the factorization is a prime, we then have an array of primes *only*. This array is called the *mosaic factorization* or simply the *mosaic* of the original integer.

As examples, in the following table we give some integers along with their standard factorization and their mosaic factorization.

TABLE 11.1

| | factorizations | |
	standard	mosaic
16	2^4	2^{2^2}
48	$2^4 \cdot 3$	$2^{2^2} \cdot 3$
162	$2 \cdot 3^4$	$2 \cdot 3^{2^2}$
175	$5^2 \cdot 7$	$5^2 \cdot 7$
5184	$2^6 \cdot 3^4$	$2^{2 \cdot 3} \cdot 3^{2^2}$
65536	2^{16}	$2^{2^{2^2}}$
262144	2^{18}	$2^{2 \cdot 3^2}$
373248	$2^9 \cdot 3^6$	$2^{3^2} \cdot 3^{2 \cdot 3}$

As exercises, find the mosaic factorizations of 496, 8128, and 29736.

Before going on, we would like to clarify a point regarding the formation of a mosaic factorization. Some mosaics have a tier type part such as 3^{2^2} or 2^{2^2}. The difficulty lies in the *association* of the primes in the tier. For example, is $2^{3^2} = 2^{(3^2)} = 2^9$ (as it is in the preceding mosaic of 373248), or is $2^{3^2} = (2^3)^2 = 2^6$? Also, in the mosaic for 65536, $2^{2^{2^2}} = 2^{(2^{(2^2)})} = 2^{(2^4)} = 2^{16}$; but could $2^{2^{2^2}} = (2^2)^{(2^2)} = (2^2)^4 = 2^8$? The alternate values arise only because we have not yet made a determination regarding the *associativity* of the primes in a tier. The reason that a choice must be made is that the operation of raising a positive integer to a positive integral power is *not* an *associative* operation, since $a^{(b^c)} \neq (a^b)^c$ for arbitrary positive integers a, b, c; in fact, it is *not* a *commutative* operation either, but that is not the reason for our difficulty (see Problem 1.6). Now, the method of forming mosaics *from the bottom up* leads us to the *opposite* choice of association among the primes when we break up a mosaic. Hence, we associate the primes from the *top down* so that the tier a^{b^c} always means $a^{(b^c)}$ and the tier $a^{b^{c^d}}$ always means $a^{(b^{(c^d)})}$. Therefore, in our earlier examples,

$$2^{3^2} = 2^{(3^2)} = 2^9 \quad \text{and} \quad 2^{2^{2^2}} = 2^{(2^{(2^2)})} = 2^{(2^4)} = 2^{16}.$$

Now suppose we look at the related problem of forming mosaics from a given set of primes. For example, from the primes 2 and 3, we obtain the three mosaics $2 \cdot 3$, 2^3, and 3^2. From the primes 2, 3, and 5, we obtain the following sixteen mosaics:

$$2 \cdot 3 \cdot 5, 2^5 \cdot 3, 2 \cdot 3^5, 2^3 \cdot 5, 2 \cdot 5^3, 3^2 \cdot 5, 3 \cdot 5^2, 2^{3 \cdot 5},$$
$$3^{2 \cdot 5}, 5^{2 \cdot 3}, 2^{3^5}, 2^{5^3}, 3^{2^5}, 3^{5^2}, 5^{3^2}, 5^{3^2}.$$

The primes 2, 2, and 3 can form the following six mosaics: $2^2 \cdot 3$, $2 \cdot 3^2$, $2^{2 \cdot 3}$, 2^{2^3}, 2^{3^2}, 3^{2^2}. Finally, the prime 7 can form only one mosaic, namely 7, and the primes 2, 2, and 2 also can form only one mosaic, namely 2^{2^2}.

As an exercise, exhibit all the mosaics that can be formed using the primes 2, 3, and 3.

THE RESIDUAL OF A MOSAIC

Suppose we multiply all the primes in a given mosaic. This product will be an integer called the *residual* of the mosaic. For example, the mosaic of $48 = 2^{2^2} \cdot 3$ yields the residual $24 = 2 \cdot 2 \cdot 2 \cdot 3$, the mosaic of $175 = 5^2 \cdot 7$ yields the residual $70 = 2 \cdot 5 \cdot 7$, and the mosaic of $5184 = 2^{2 \cdot 3} \cdot 3^{2^2}$ yields the residual $144 = 2 \cdot 2 \cdot 2 \cdot 2 \cdot 3 \cdot 3$. As exercises, find the residual of each of the mosaics given in Table 11.1.

Note that the residuals of the mosaics of 48, 162, and 262144 are equal. This can happen, since the residual is the product of all the primes that appear in a mosaic *ignoring* their position in the mosaic. In fact, in a preceding example, we gave sixteen mosaics formed from 2, 3, and 5, and each one has the residual 30. As an exercise, construct every mosaic that has a residual equal to 20 and find the corresponding integers.

We have now given you most of the elementary facts on the mosaic factorization of an integer. There are a few other interesting properties that we have included in the problems that follow this section.

PROBLEMS

11.1 Find the mosaic factorization of each of the following integers.
   (a) 3600
   (b) 25900
   (c) 372800
   (d) 2^{48}
   (e) 56940
   (f) 181800

11.2 Find the mosaic factorization of each of the following integers.
   (a) 398144
   (b) 311400
   (c) 751440
   (d) 1,037,760
   (e) 2^{3600}

11.3 Write as many mosaics as possible from each of the given sets of primes.
   (a) 5, 7
   (b) 5, 5, 7
   (c)* 5, 5, 7, 7
   (d) 3, 5, 7
   (e) 5, 5, 5, 5, 5

11.4 Find the integer corresponding to each of the following mosaics.
(a) $3^2 \cdot 3 5^2$
(b) $2^{3^2} \cdot 3^{2^3}$
(c) $2^{2^2 \cdot 3}$
(d) $3^{2^{2^2}}$
(e) $2^{2^3} \cdot 3^{2^2}$

11.5 Find the residual of each of the mosaics of the integers given in Problem 11.1.

11.6 In each of the following, find all the integers with mosaics having the given integer as the residual.
(a) 12
(b) 18
(c) 24
(d)* 36

11.7 (a) Find all the mosaics that have the residual 16.
(b) Find all the mosaics that have the residual 70.

11.8 Find all the mosaics that can be formed by using:
(a) two distinct primes p and q with p less than q
(b) three primes p, q, and q again, where p is less than q
(c) three distinct primes p, q, and r with p less than q and q less than r.

11.9 Let n be any positive integer greater than 1. Prove that
(a) n has a mosaic factorization
(b)* the residual of the mosaic of n must always be less than or equal to n (Appendix)
(c)* if n is not divisible by a perfect square, the residual of the mosaic of n equals n. Is the converse of this statement true? (Appendix)

11.10 Suppose we denote by $(n)'$ the number that is the residual of the mosaic of n. For example, $(6)' = 6$, $(9)' = 6$, $(48)' = 24$, $(175)' = 70$, and $(5184)' = 144$. Compute
(a) $(144)'$
(b) $(496)'$
(c) $(8128)'$

11.11 (a) Compute $((48)(162))'$ and show that it is *less* than $(48)' \cdot (162)'$.
(b) Find two other numbers a and b such that $(ab)'$ is less than $(a)' \cdot (b)'$.

11.12 (a) Compute $((2)(2^{16}))'$ and show that it is *greater* than $(2)' \cdot (2^{16})'$.
(b) Find two other numbers a and b such that $(ab)'$ is greater than $(a)' \cdot (b)'$.

11.13 (a) Show that $((24)(35))' = (24)' \cdot (35)'$.
(b) Show that $((12)(25))' = (12)' \cdot (25)'$.
(c) Find two other numbers a and b such that $(ab)' = (a)' \cdot (b)'$.
(d)* Prove that if a and b are relatively prime, then $(ab)' = (a)' \cdot (b)'$ (Appendix).
(e)* Is the converse of the statement in (d) true? (Appendix)

11.14* It is clear that only one mosaic can be formed with a single prime p. In Problem 11.8, the student found that exactly three mosaics can be made by using two distinct primes p and q, while exactly sixteen mosaics can be formed by using three distinct primes p, q, and r. With these results, the student should now attempt to show that precisely

125 mosaics can be made by using four distinct primes p, q, r, and s. Finally, observe that the preceding answers were $1 = 2^0$ for one prime, $3 = 3^1$ for *two* primes, $16 = 4^2$ for *three* primes, and $125 = 5^3$ for *four* primes. Would the student care to guess at the number of mosaics that can be made by using *five* distinct primes? by using k distinct primes for any positive integer k?

Section *12*

PERFECT NUMBERS

In this section, we apply the standard factorization of an integer to the study of a rather small but curious class of numbers called *perfect* numbers. Mathematicians have searched for numbers of this type for over 2000 years, yet to date only 23 have been found. No single topic in all of number theory has spurred so much research in every direction with such a wide variety of results. Even though the perfect numbers themselves have been elusive, the search for them has provided us with a wealth of number theoretic knowledge. Thus, without the stimulus that the perfect numbers supplied, many important results in number theory might never have been discovered. We now proceed to a discussion of the general theory of perfect numbers.

Let n be any integer greater than 1. Let σ_n (pronounced "sigma sub n") equal the *sum* of all the positive divisors of n that are *less* than n. For example,

$$\sigma_5 = 1,$$
$$\sigma_6 = 1 + 2 + 3 = 6,$$
$$\sigma_9 = 1 + 3 = 4,$$
$$\sigma_{11} = 1,$$
$$\sigma_{12} = 1 + 2 + 3 + 4 + 6 = 16,$$
$$\sigma_{17} = 1,$$
$$\sigma_{20} = 1 + 2 + 4 + 5 + 10 = 22,$$
$$\sigma_{26} = 1 + 2 + 13 = 16,$$
$$\sigma_{28} = 1 + 2 + 4 + 7 + 14 = 28,$$
$$\sigma_{30} = 1 + 2 + 3 + 5 + 6 + 10 + 15 = 42.$$

Observe that $\sigma_p = 1$ for every prime p since 1 is the only positive divisor of p that is less than p. If n is not a prime, we see from the preceding examples that σ_n may be *less* than, *greater* than, or *equal* to n. Note that when an integer n has many divisors, σ_n is usually greater than n (see the preceding examples for $n = 12$, $n = 20$, $n = 30$); and when n has few divisors, σ_n is usually less than n (see the preceding examples for $n = 9$, $n = 26$). There are also integers n for which $\sigma_n = n$ (see the preceding examples for $n = 6$, $n = 28$); such numbers are *extremely rare* however and are called *perfect* numbers.

The student should verify that the only perfect numbers less than 30 are 6 and 28. Now, if the student attempts to find the third perfect number by checking the sum of the divisors of integers greater than 30, he is in for quite a surprise. In fact, the third perfect number is 496, which is substantially larger than 28. If we go even further and attempt to find the fourth perfect number, we must go all the way to 8128. As exercises, the student should prove that 496 and 8128 are indeed perfect numbers by showing that $\sigma_{496} = 496$ and $\sigma_{8128} = 8128$.

In order to convince the student of the rarity of perfect numbers, we give the fifth one, 33,550,336, and the sixth one, 8,589,869,056. In fact, the twenty-third perfect number has slightly more than 6700 digits and it would take approximately two and a half pages of this textbook to write it. It is not even known whether there are finitely many or infinitely many perfect numbers.

Also note that the six previously mentioned perfect numbers are *even* numbers ending in 6 or 28. It is also true that the remaining seventeen are *even* numbers ending in 6 or 28. It is not yet known whether there are any *odd* perfect numbers. However, it has been shown that if there is an *odd* perfect number, it must be *greater* than 10^{36}. Therefore, if an *odd* perfect number exists, it must have at least 37 digits.

A MAJOR THEOREM ON PERFECT NUMBERS

We begin with the standard factorization of the first five perfect numbers. Then we alter the odd prime factor and rewrite it as a power of 2 less the number 1, obtaining

$$P_1 = 6 = 2 \cdot 3 = 2(2^2 - 1)$$
$$P_2 = 28 = 2^2 \cdot 7 = 2^2(2^3 - 1)$$
$$P_3 = 496 = 2^4 \cdot 31 = 2^4(2^5 - 1)$$
$$P_4 = 8128 = 2^6 \cdot 127 = 2^6(2^7 - 1)$$
$$P_5 = 33,550,336 = 2^{12} \cdot 8191 = 2^{12}(2^{13} - 1).$$

Note that in each instance, the factored number has the form $2^{p-1}(2^p - 1)$ where p is a prime and where $2^p - 1$ is also a prime. This leads us to the proof of the theorem that states that *every* number of this form is an *even* perfect number. This result along with the definition of a perfect number appeared in Book IX of Euclid's *Elements* about 300 B.C. It can also be shown that the *converse* of this result is true, that is, every *even* perfect number must have this form. The converse was proved over 2000 years later in 1757 by the Swiss mathematician Leonhard Euler.

As a consequence of these results, we see that the problem of finding even perfect numbers reduces to the one of finding primes p such that $2^p - 1$ is also a prime. Note that the number $2^{10}(2^{11} - 1)$ is not on the list of perfect numbers even though 11 is a prime. The reason is that $2^{11} - 1 = (23)(89)$ and is *not* a prime. Unfortunately, the problem of determining all primes p such that $2^p - 1$ is also a prime is another *unsolved* problem. The primes of the form $2^p - 1$ are called Mersenne primes after the French friar and amateur mathematician Marin Mersenne. He discussed these primes in one of his works in 1644 and made conjectures about them. Some of his conjectures were later shown to be true while others were shown to be false. For example, Mersenne conjectured that $2^{31} - 1$ was a prime and he was proven *right* by Euler in 1772; he also conjectured that $2^{67} - 1$ was a prime and he was proven *wrong* in 1903 when the factor 193,707,721 was discovered by the American mathematician F. N. Cole. At present, twenty-three Mersenne primes have been found along with their associated perfect numbers, but no one knows whether there are finitely or infinitely many of these primes. The twenty-third prime of this type is $2^{11213} - 1$. It has over 3300 digits and it would take a little more than one page of this textbook to write it. It is, at present, the largest known prime, and the corresponding perfect number $2^{11212}(2^{11213} - 1)$ is the twenty-third and largest known perfect number.

12.1 Theorem   Let p be a prime such that the number $2^p - 1$ is also a prime. Let $K = 2^{p-1}(2^p - 1)$. Then K is a perfect number.

Before presenting the general proof, we will give an example. Suppose we take $P_3 = 496 = 2^4(2^5 - 1)$ and prove that it is a perfect number. Now, the powers of 2 which divide 496 are $2^0 = 1, 2, 2^2, 2^3$, and 2^4. The prime $31 = 2^5 - 1$ also divides 496, along with the products $2(31)$, $2^2(31), 2^3(31)$, and $2^4(31)$. Since these are the only positive divisors, the sum of *all* the positive divisors of 496 is $1 + 2 + 2^2 + 2^3 + 2^4 + 31 + 2(31) + 2^2(31) + 2^3(31) + 2^4(31) = 1 + 2 + 2^2 + 2^3 + 2^4 + (31)(1 + 2 + 2^2 + 2^3 + 2^4)$. However, from the formula for the sum of a geometric progression, $1 + 2 + 2^2 + 2^3 + 2^4 = \dfrac{2^5 - 1}{2 - 1} = 2^5 - 1$. $\Big($Recall that the formula states that the sum of a geometric progression with first term a, last term L, and common ratio r is $\dfrac{rL - a}{r - 1}$. $\Big)$ Therefore, the sum of all the divisors of 496 reduces to $(2^5 - 1) + (31)(2^5 - 1) = (2^5 - 1)(1 + 31) = 2^5(2^5 - 1) = 2(2^4(2^5 - 1)) = 2(496)$. However, in adding the divisors of 496, we included the number $2^4(31)$ which equals 496. Therefore, $\sigma_{496} = 2(496) - 496 = 496$, and hence 496 is a perfect number.

We shall now imitate the above argument and obtain the proof of the aforementioned theorem.

Proof Since $K = 2^{p-1}(2^p - 1)$, the powers of 2 which divide K are $2^0 = 1, 2, 2^2, 2^3, \ldots, 2^{p-2}, 2^{p-1}$. The prime $2^p - 1$ also divides K and all the products $2(2^p - 1), 2^2(2^p - 1), \ldots, 2^{p-1}(2^p - 1)$ divide K. Since these are the only positive divisors of K, the sum of *all* the positive divisors of K is $1 + 2 + 2^2 + \ldots + 2^{p-1} + (2^p - 1)(1 + 2 + 2^2 + \ldots + 2^{p-1})$. Once again, using the formula for the sum of a geometric progression, we find that $1 + 2 + 2^2 + \ldots + 2^{p-1} = \dfrac{2^p - 1}{2 - 1} = 2^p - 1$. Therefore, the sum of all the positive divisors of K is $(2^p - 1) + (2^p - 1)(2^p - 1) = (2^p - 1)(1 + 2^p - 1) = 2^p(2^p - 1) = 2(2^{p-1}(2^p - 1)) = 2K$. But we included $2^{p-1}(2^p - 1) = K$ as one of the divisors of K. Therefore, $\sigma_K = 2K - K = K$, and K is a perfect number.

In closing this section, it is worth noting that despite Theorem 12.1 and its converse, relatively few perfect numbers have been found. The first four were certainly known in Euclid's time. From then to the middle of the twentieth century, only eight more were found. These were discovered by some brilliant men using ingenious methods of hand calculation. Thus, only twelve perfect numbers were known prior to 1950. However, since the advent of high-speed electronic computers, eleven more have been discovered, the last one in 1964. Thus, with the aid of computers, mathematicians have found almost as many perfect numbers since 1950 as they were able to find in the twenty centuries prior to 1950. Certainly this search is far from over. It is likely that other even perfect numbers having an astounding number of digits will be discovered soon. It is also possible that someone may prove that there are infinitely many perfect numbers, without actually producing a formula for finding them. Perhaps the student now appreciates Theorem 8.2 in which we established that *there are infinitely many primes.* That theorem enables us to say that there *are* infinitely many primes even though the largest one known is $2^{11213} - 1$. We know that this prime is *not* the last one even though we may not be able to produce the next one. With perfect numbers, we have no such theorem; the last one that was discovered really could be the last perfect number. Also there is still a remote possibility that someone will find an *odd* perfect number that has 37 or more digits. Up to now, the number theorists have exhibited a variety of conditions that odd perfect numbers must satisfy *if* they exist and, unfortunately, the conditions are not incompatible with one another. Thus, mathematicians have built a theory for the class of odd perfect numbers without even knowing that they exist. The more conditions that are found, the better the chance of obtaining contradictory conditions. Such contradictions would rule out the existence of odd perfect numbers altogether, and would put us in the peculiar position of having a whole theory built up for a class of numbers that does not exist.

PROBLEMS

12.1 (a) Find all the positive divisors of each of the following integers, and prove that they are *not* perfect numbers by showing $\sigma_n \neq n$: 120, 1116, $2^{10}(2^{11} - 1)$.

    (b) Find seven non-prime positive integers $n < 100$ such that $\sigma_n < n$.

    (c) Find seven positive integers $n < 100$ such that $\sigma_n > n$.

12.2 (a) Is there a perfect number between each power of 10?

    (b) Do the perfect numbers end alternately in 6 and 28?

12.3 Suppose p is a prime and n is a positive integer. Prove that p^n is *not* a perfect number.

12.4 In the case of the first four perfect numbers, show that the *sum* of the *reciprocals* of *all* the *divisors* of the number that are greater than 1 equals 1. (For example, all the divisors of 6 that are greater than 1 are 2, 3, and 6. The sum of their reciprocals is $\frac{1}{2} + \frac{1}{3} + \frac{1}{6} = 1$.)

12.5* Prove that if K is any *even* perfect number, the sum of the reciprocals of all the divisors of K that are greater than 1 equals 1.

12.6 A positive integer n is called *pluperfect* if $\sigma_n = kn$ where k is an integer greater than or equal to 2. Prove that 120, 672, and 30240 are pluperfect numbers.

12.7 A number m is called a *magic* number if, when we add its digits and then add the digits of the resulting sum, and so on, we finally obtain the sum 1. For example, 298 has the sum of its digits equal to $2 + 9 + 8 = 19$. Then the sum of the digits of 19 is $1 + 9 = 10$. Finally, the sum of the digits in 10 is $1 + 0 = 1$.

    (a) Show that the first six perfect numbers except 6 are also magic numbers.

    (b) Find ten magic numbers that are not perfect numbers.

12.8 A positive integer n is called a *multiplicatively perfect* number if it is equal to the *product* of all of its divisors that are less than n. Prove each of the following statements.

    (a) 6, 35, and 143 are multiplicatively perfect numbers.

    (b) If n is the product of *two* distinct primes, n is multiplicatively perfect.

    (c) 8, 27, and 125 are multiplicatively perfect.

    (d) If $n = p^3$ where p is a prime, n is multiplicatively perfect.

12.9 Find each of the following:

    (a) the g.c.d. of 496 and 8128 (see Section 10)

    (b) the l.c.m. of 496 and 8128

(c) the number of positive divisors of 496; the number of positive divisors of 8128 (see Section 9)

(d) the number of positive divisors of the product (496)(8128).

12.10* Let a and b be two distinct even perfect numbers with $a > b$ where $a = 2^{p-1}(2^p - 1)$ and $b = 2^{q-1}(2^q - 1)$. Find each of the following:

(a) the g.c.d. of a and b (see Section 10)

(b) the l.c.m. of a and b

(c) the number of positive divisors of a; the number of positive divisors of b (see Section 9)

(d) the number of positive divisors of the product ab

(e) how many positive divisors does the product (8128)(33,550,336) have?

12.11 **(a)** Show that for $n = 1, 2, 3, 4, 5, 6,$ and 7 the expression $2^{2n}(2^{2n+1} - 1)$ yields a number that ends in 6 or 28.

(b) How many of the numbers found in (a) are perfect?

(c) What is the connection between the expression given in (a) and the form of an even perfect number?

12.12 **(a)** Write the first four perfect numbers in the base 2 (see Section 4) and compare them.

(b) Describe the product $2^{2n}(2^{2n+1} - 1)$ in the base 2 where n is a positive integer.

(c) Write the perfect numbers 28, 496, and 8128 in the base 4 and compare them.

(d) Describe the product $2^{2n}(2^{2n+1} - 1)$ in the base 4 where n is a positive integer.

(e) Using the results in parts (b) and (d), write the fifth perfect number in the base 2 and the base 4.

12.13 Let the symbol $(n)^+$ denote the sum of *all* the positive divisors of n *including* n itself. Then $(n)^+ = \sigma_n + n$ for every positive integer n, $(p)^+ = 1 + p$ for every prime p, and if n is any even perfect number, $(n)^+ = 2n$. Compute each of the following:

(a) $(60)^+$

(b) $(144)^+$

(c) $(360)^+$

(d) $(p^i)^+$ for any prime p and any positive integer i

(e)* $(p^i q^j)^+$ where p and q are distinct primes and i and j are positive integers (Appendix)

(f)* $(p^i q^j r^k)^+$ where p, q, and r are distinct primes and $i, j,$ and k are positive integers. (Appendix)

12.14 **(a)** Compute $((5)(15))^+$ and show that it is *less* than $(5)^+ \cdot (15)^+$.

(b) Find two other numbers a and b such that $(ab)^+ < (a)^+ \cdot (b)^+$.

12.15 **(a)** Show that $((9)(25))^+ = (9)^+ \cdot (25)^+$.

(b) Show that $((13)(27))^+ = (13)^+ \cdot (27)^+$.

(c) Find two other numbers a and b such that $(ab)^+ = (a)^+ \cdot (b)^+$.

(d)* Prove that if a and b are relatively prime, then $(ab)^+ = (a)^+ \cdot (b)^+$. (*Hint.* $(a, b) = 1$ implies that the standard factorizations of a and b have no primes in common. Therefore, in forming the product ab, none of the exponents can combine. This means that the standard factorization of the product ab is just a copy of the standard factorizations of a and b put together. Now use a generalization of the result in Problem 12.13(f).)

(e) Is the converse of the statement in (d) true?

II

ALGEBRAIC SYSTEMS

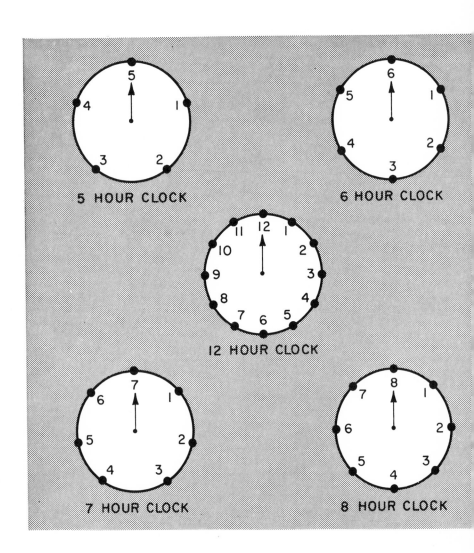

5 HOUR CLOCK

6 HOUR CLOCK

12 HOUR CLOCK

7 HOUR CLOCK

8 HOUR CLOCK

Section *13*

CLOCK ARITHMETIC

Thus far, we have dealt mostly with the *infinite* system of integers and we have studied many of its properties. In Section 7, we briefly studied algebras consisting of the *divisors* of an integer *n*. These were our only examples of *finite* algebraic systems. The elements in these algebras were denoted by integers, and the operations that were defined depended on the concept of the g.c.d. and the l.c.m. of two integers. Now we introduce the student to another collection of *finite* algebraic systems. The elements in these new algebras are also denoted by integers, but the operations that are defined are *related* to the ordinary addition and multiplication of integers. These new algebras are called *modular systems* and their special kind of arithmetic is called *modular* arithmetic. In comparison to some of the material studied in the earlier sections, the modular systems are a recent development in mathematics. The first publication of these systems occurred in 1801 and, from that point on, the study of algebra and number theory was revolutionized. The modular systems provided the impetus that eventually drove number theory into its modern era. The development of the modular systems as presented in this section and the following ones is more elementary than the original, but still contains the essential ingredients of the original development.

As an introduction, we shall discuss the modular system associated with telling time on a clock with its face divided into six units of time. We use the integers 1, 2, 3, 4, 5, and 6 to label the clock dial (see Fig. 13.1).

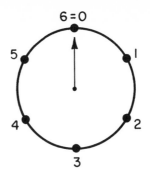

Figure 13.1

The point at 6 has also been labeled zero as well, since it is the starting point for each rotation of the pointer in a clockwise direction. What kind of arithmetic is done on this clock dial? Suppose the pointer is at 2, and then 3 more units of time pass; we rotate the pointer in a clockwise direction to 5; hence, we added 3 and 2 and obtained 5. Similarly, if the pointer is at 1 and 4 units of time pass, we rotate the pointer to 5, which is $1 + 4$. Now suppose the pointer is at 4, and 5 units of time pass; we rotate the pointer 5 units in a clockwise direction, ending up at 3. But $3 \neq 4 + 5$ under integer addition; hence, the arithmetic on the clock dial *differs* from our usual arithmetic. As another example, if the pointer is at 5, and 3 units of time expire, we rotate the pointer to 2. Note that $2 \neq 5 + 3$ under integer addition. To exaggerate the situation, if the pointer is at 4, and 49 units of time elapse, the pointer ends up at 5 after 8 complete revolutions about the clock dial. What happens is that each time you pass 6 or zero, you begin counting at 1 again. In the preceding case, the pointer passed 6 or zero a total of 8 times before stopping at 5. Consequently, in this system, whenever we add units of time, we obtain only the numbers 6 or 0, 1, 2, 3, 4, and 5. These elements form a system that is *closed* under addition and we call it the *modulo-six system*.

It turns out that we can also *multiply* elements in this system by using the following definition. For any elements a and b, the product

$$ab = \overbrace{b + b + b + \ldots + b}^{a \text{ terms}}.$$ Therefore, $5 \cdot 3 = 3 + 3 + 3 + 3 + 3 = 3$, while $3 \cdot 5 = 5 + 5 + 5 = 3$. As other examples, $4 \cdot 5 = 5 + 5 + 5 + 5 = 2$ and $4 \cdot 3 = 3 + 3 + 3 + 3 = 0 = 6$. Hence, multiplication is simply defined in terms of addition, and thus, knowing how to add, we also know how to multiply. Consequently, this modulo-six system is *closed* under *multiplication* as well as under addition.

Note also that whenever 6 or zero is added to an element, the element remains unchanged. For example, $3 + 6 = 3$ and $3 + 0 = 3$. Observe that $3 + 6$ indicates one complete revolution beginning and ending at 3, while $3 + 0$ indicates no rotation of the pointer at all. However, the end result is the same, since we look only at the position of the pointer after the rotation corresponding to the number being added. In a similar way, it can be shown that $a + 6 = a + 0 = a$ for each of the elements in the modulo-six system. Hence, 6 or 0 behaves like an *additive identity* in this system. Since we would like to maintain the notion of 0 as the additive identity, we shall stop using the number 6 and consider the modulo-six system to be composed of the numbers 0, 1, 2, 3, 4, and 5.

With regard to multiplication, we see that $1 \cdot 5 = 5$ and $5 \cdot 1 = 1 + 1 + 1 + 1 + 1 = 5$, and for any other element a in the modulo-six system, $1 \cdot a = a \cdot 1 = a$. Hence, 1 is the *multiplicative identity* of the system.

Consequently, the modulo-six system satisfies several properties that the integers also satisfy. We have *closure* under *addition* and *multiplication*, and an *additive* and a *multiplicative identity* exists.

In Tables 13.1 and 13.2, we give incomplete tables for the addition and multiplication of the elements in the modulo-six system. As exer-

TABLE 13.1
MODULO-SIX
ADDITION TABLE

+	0	1	2	3	4	5
0	0	1	2	3	4	5
1	1	2				0
2	2		4			1
3	3			0		2
4	4				2	3
5	5	0	1	2	3	4

TABLE 13.2
MODULO-SIX
MULTIPLICATION TABLE

·	0	1	2	3	4	5
0	0	0	0	0	0	0
1	0	1	2	3	4	5
2	0	2	4			
3	0	3		3		
4	0	4			4	
5	0	5				1

cises, the student should fill in the blank spaces in the tables and then verify that the *commutative* law holds for *addition* and *multiplication*.

If the student consults the completed addition table, it becomes clear that each element has an *additive inverse*. Since $2 + 4 = 0$, we can state that $-2 = 4$ or that $2 = -4$; since $1 + 5 = 0$, we can state that $-1 = 5$ or that $1 = -5$, and so on. In this context, the minus sign means the *additive inverse* of the number that follows it, just as it does in the system of integers. If the student consults the completed multiplication table, he will notice that not every element has a *multiplicative inverse*. In fact, only 1 and 5 have multiplicative inverses and each is its own inverse since $1 \cdot 1 = 1$ and $5 \cdot 5 = 1$. We shall soon study the modulo-seven system as an example of a system in which *every* nonzero element does have a multiplicative inverse.

Finally, for the sake of completeness, the student should test each of the following rules in a few cases using specific numbers from the modulo-six system in place of the letters *a*, *b*, and *c*.

1. The *associative* law for *addition*, i.e., $(a + b) + c = a + (b + c)$
2. The *associative* law for *multiplication*, i.e., $(ab)c = a(bc)$
3. The *distributive* law, i.e., $a(b + c) = ab + ac$

This new kind of arithmetic was based on a 6-unit clock, but it can also be extended to other modular systems under similar conditions. For example, if we have a 7-unit clock, we use the clock dial shown in Fig. 13.2 and we have the *modulo-seven system*.

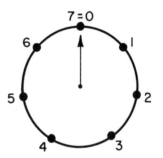

Figure 13.2

Adding 2 and 3 yields 5 in this system, while $3 + 5$ yields 1 (since adding 5 to 3 brings the pointer past zero to 1 unit beyond zero). We can also multiply in this system, for example, $3 \cdot 4 = 4 + 4 + 4 = 5$ and $2 \cdot 6 = 6 + 6 = 5$. Observe that the modulo-seven system consists of the elements $7 = 0, 1, 2, 3, 4, 5, 6$ and, under the clock arithmetic, we have a system that is *closed* under *addition* and *multiplication*. Once again, to maintain 0 as the *identity element* under *addition*, we drop 7 and use only 0 as the first element in the modulo-seven system. Note also that 1 is the *multiplicative identity element*.

We now give incomplete tables for the addition and multiplication of the elements in the modulo-seven system in Tables 13.3 and 13.4. If the student completes the tables by filling in the blanks, it will become clear that the *commutative* laws for *addition* and *multiplication* hold in this system. Finally, the student should test, in a few specific cases, the *associative* laws for *addition* and *multiplication* and the *distributive* law.

TABLE 13.3
MODULO-SEVEN
ADDITION TABLE

+	0	1	2	3	4	5	6
0	0	1	2	3	4	5	6
1	1	2					0
2	2		4				1
3	3			6			2
4	4				1		3
5	5					3	4
6	6	0	1	2	3	4	5

TABLE 13.4
MODULO-SEVEN
MULTIPLICATION TABLE

·	0	1	2	3	4	5	6
0	0	0	0	0	0	0	0
1	0	1	2	3	4	5	6
2	0	2	4				
3	0	3		2			
4	0	4			2		
5	0	5				4	
6	0	6					1

If the student checks the completed tables, he will find an *additive inverse* for each element and a *multiplicative inverse* for each *nonzero* element. For example, $4 + 3 = 0$; therefore, $-4 = 3$ and $4 = -3$; $2 + 5 = 0$; hence, $-2 = 5$ and $2 = -5$. Under multiplication, $2 \cdot 4 = 1$; therefore, 4 is the multiplicative inverse of 2, and 2 is the multiplicative inverse of 4; $3 \cdot 5 = 1$, and so 5 is the multiplicative inverse of 3, and 3 is the multiplicative inverse of 5.

In some of the problems that follow, we will introduce the student to a few more modular systems in which clock arithmetic can be applied. In the next section, we will generalize the concepts presented thus far, and we will go into a more detailed and systematic analysis of clock arithmetic as it is applied to arbitrary modular systems.

PROBLEMS

13.1 Using Tables 13.1 and 13.2, find each of the following in the modulo-six system.

    (a) $3 \cdot 2 + 4 \cdot 3$ **(b)** $5(3 \cdot 2) + (4 \cdot 2) \cdot 3$

    (c) $(3 \cdot 5 + 2 \cdot 4) + 4 \cdot 3$ **(d)** $3(2 + 4)$

13.2 Using Tables 13.3 and 13.4, find each of the following in the modulo-seven system.

    (a) $3 \cdot 6 + 6 \cdot 5$ **(b)** $(4 \cdot 5) \cdot 6 + 2(3 + 4)$

    (c) $2 \cdot 3 + (3 \cdot 4 + 4 \cdot 5)$ **(d)** $6(5 + 3)$

13.3 In the modulo-six system, show that 0, 2, 3, and 4 do not have multiplicative inverses. (*Hint.* In the case of the element 2, show that $2x = 1$ has no solution for any element x in the system.)

13.4 Find the multiplicative inverse of each nonzero element in the modulo-seven system.

13.5 **(a)** In the modulo-seven system, is it true that $ab = 0$ implies that $a = 0$ or $b = 0$?

    (b) In the modulo-six system, is it true that $ab = 0$ implies that $a = 0$ or $b = 0$?

13.6 **(a)** Construct addition and multiplication tables for the modulo-five system which consists of 0, 1, 2, 3, and 4.

    (b) Find the additive inverse of each element.

    (c) Find the multiplicative inverse of each nonzero element.

    (d) Compute $3(4 + 2)$ and $2 \cdot 3 + 4 \cdot 2$.

13.7 **(a)** Construct addition and multiplication tables for the modulo-eight system which consists of 0, 1, 2, 3, 4, 5, 6, and 7.

    (b) Find the additive inverse of each element.

    (c) If possible, find the multiplicative inverse of each nonzero element.

    (d) Compute $3(7 + 4)$ and $5 \cdot 4 + 3 \cdot 7$.

13.8 **(a)** In the modulo-five system, is it true that $ab = 0$ implies that $a = 0$ or $b = 0$?

    (b) In the modulo-eight system, is it true that $ab = 0$ implies that $a = 0$ or $b = 0$?

13.9 How can we define subtraction in clock arithmetic? Guess at a definition and then compute $5 - 3$ and $3 - 5$ in both the modulo-six and modulo-seven systems.

13.10 In the modulo-five system, suppose we define $\sqrt{a}$ as a number b with the property that $b \cdot b = a$. If possible, find $\sqrt{a}$ for each number a in the modulo-five system (Appendix).

13.11 In the modulo-five system, suppose we define $\sqrt[3]{a}$ as a number b with the property that $b \cdot b \cdot b = a$. If possible, find $\sqrt[3]{a}$ for each number a in the modulo-five system (Appendix).

13.12 Find the *sum* of all the elements in
(a) the modulo-six system
(b) the modulo-eight system.

13.13 Find the *sum* of all the elements in
(a) the modulo-five system
(b) the modulo-seven system.

13.14 Find the *product* of all the nonzero elements in
(a) the modulo-six system
(b) the modulo-eight system.

13.15 Find the *product* of all the nonzero elements in
(a) the modulo-five system
(b) the modulo-seven system.

13.16 Suppose we number the hours in a day as they do in the military: 1:00 AM as 1, 2:00 AM as 2,..., 12:00 noon as 12, 1:00 PM as 13, 2:00 PM as 14,..., 11:00 PM as 23, and 12 midnight as 24 or 0. We then have a 24-hour clock. Answer each of the following questions using clock arithmetic.
(a) If it is 9:00 PM, what time is it 30 hours later?
(b) If it is 9:00 AM, what time is it 40 hours later?
(c) If it is 3:00 PM, what time is it 50 hours later?

13.17 Suppose we number the days of the week in the following way: Sunday, 1; Monday, 2; Tuesday, 3; Wednesday, 4; Thursday, 5; Friday, 6; Saturday, 7. We now have a 7-day clock. Answer each of the following questions using clock arithmetic.
(a) If it is Tuesday, what day is it 30 days later?
(b) If it is Thursday, what day is it 40 days later?
(c) If it is Friday, what day is it 50 days later?

13.18 Suppose we number the months of the year in the usual way, beginning with January as the first month and ending with December as the twelfth. We then have a 12-month clock. Answer each of the following questions using clock arithmetic.
(a) If it is July, what month is it 29 months later?
(b) If it is March, what month is it 33 months later?
(c) If it is April, what month is it 45 months later?

THE ALGEBRA OF REMAINDERS

Notation   We shall denote the modulo-six system by R_6, the modulo-seven system by R_7, the modulo-five system by R_5, and the modulo-eight system by R_8. In general, if n is any positive integer greater than 1, we shall denote the modulo-n system by R_n where R_n consists of the elements 0, 1, 2, 3, 4, . . . , $n - 2$, $n - 1$. Finally, the set of all integers 0, ± 1, ± 2, ± 3, ± 4, ± 5, . . . will be denoted by Z.

ARITHMETIC IN THE R_n SYSTEMS

The "clock" method explained in Section 13 for addition and multiplication in R_6 and R_7 is easily extended to R_5 and R_8 in the problems following that section. However, for larger integers such as 27, 105, 1122, and so on, this method is a tedious one. We shall now give a more practical method of addition and multiplication in the R_n systems, a method that will enable us to calculate in R_n systems no matter how large n is.

By using the "clock" method in R_7, we see that $5 + 6 = 4$. Now, if we add 5 and 6 as integers in Z, we obtain 11. Dividing by 7 (using the Division Algorithm), we obtain $11 = 1 \cdot 7 + 4$. Note that the remainder 4 is precisely $5 + 6$ in R_7, while the quotient 1 indicates the number of times we pass 0 on the clock dial when adding 5 and 6 by the "clock" method. If we multiply 5 and 6 in R_7, we obtain $5 \times 6 = 6 + 6 + 6 + 6 + 6 = 2$ by the "clock" method. Now, if we multiply

5 and 6 as integers in Z, we obtain 30. Dividing by 7, we arrive at $30 = 4 \cdot 7 + 2$. Note that the remainder 2 is precisely 5×6 in R_7, while the quotient 4 indicates the number of times we pass 0 on the clock dial when we compute $6 + 6 + 6 + 6 + 6$ by the "clock" method. As further examples, consider $2 + 4$ and 2×4 in R_7. As integers in Z, $2 + 4 = 6$. Dividing 6 by 7, we obtain $6 = 0 \cdot 7 + 6$ and so, in R_7, $2 + 4$ is also 6. Now, $2 \times 4 = 8$ in Z, and dividing by 7, we obtain a remainder of 1. Hence, $2 \times 4 = 1$ in R_7.

If the student checks the remaining entries in Tables 13.3 and 13.4 in the text, he can verify that all of the answers can be obtained by addition and multiplication in Z *followed* by a division by 7, with the *remainder* being the answer given in the tables. Since the Division Algorithm states that the only remainders possible after a division by 7 are 0, 1, 2, 3, 4, 5, 6, these are precisely the elements of R_7. The reason we ignore the quotients is that the quotients simply indicate the number of times we pass 0 on the clock dial when adding and multiplying in R_7 by the "clock" method.

The student should also compute by this method the addition and multiplication tables for R_5 and R_8 which were to be computed by the "clock" method in Problems 13.6 and 13.7. As examples in R_5, consider the following computations: $4 + 3 = 7$ in Z, dividing by 5, the remainder is 2, and so in R_5, $4 + 3 = 2$; $4 \times 3 = 12$ in Z, dividing by 5, the remainder is 2, and so in R_5, $4 \times 3 = 2$. As examples in R_8, we exhibit the following computations: $5 + 7 = 12$ in Z, dividing by 8 yields a remainder of 4, and therefore in R_8, $5 + 7 = 4$; $5 \times 7 = 35$ in Z, dividing by 8 yields a remainder of 3, and thus in R_8, $5 \times 7 = 3$. If we use the "clock" method to do the last calculation in R_8, how many times do we pass 0 on the clock dial?

THE GENERAL METHOD

Let a and b be any elements of $R_n = \{0, 1, 2, \ldots, n - 1\}$. We define $a + b$ in R_n to be the number r that is the *remainder* when $a + b$ in Z is divided by n. Similarly, we define $a \times b$ in R_n to be the number s that is the *remainder* when $a \times b$ in Z is divided by n. Then, by the Division Algorithm, both r and s are greater than or equal to zero and less than or equal to $n - 1$, and so r and s belong to R_n. Consequently, R_n *is closed under addition and multiplication*. It is also true that in R_n, the *commutative* and *associative* laws for *addition* and *multiplication*, and the *distributive* law are satisfied. This follows from the fact that each of the following equalities holds in Z: $a + b = b + a$, $ab = ba$, $a + (b + c) = (a + b) + c$, $a(bc) = (ab)c$, $a(b + c) = ab + ac$; and thus in each case, the number on the left of the equal sign has the same remainder when it is divided by n as has the number on the right. Therefore, each of the equalities holds in R_n as well as in Z.

Now, 0 and 1 both belong to R_n, and consequently R_n has *additive identity 0* and *multiplicative identity 1*. The student should verify this by applying the definition of addition and multiplication in R_n to the expressions $0 + a$ and $1 \times a$, respectively.

The *additive inverse* of an element a in R_n is an element a' satisfying the condition $a + a' = 0$. We denote a' by the more familiar $-a$. If $a = 0$, then $a' = 0$, i.e., $-0 = 0$ in R_n. If $a \neq 0$, then $a' = n - a$ since $a + (n - a) = n$ in Z, and dividing by n, we obtain the remainder 0. Therefore, when $a \neq 0$, $a + (n - a) = 0$ in R_n and $-a = n - a$. Note that $1 \leq a \leq n - 1$ and so $1 \leq n - a \leq n - 1$. Therefore, $-a$ is in R_n for every a in R_n and the *inverse property under addition* is satisfied.

SUBTRACTION IN R_n

We just saw that every element in R_n has an *additive inverse*. Now we define the operation of *subtraction* in R_n in the following way: for any two elements a and b in R_n, $a - b = a + (-b)$. Hence, the *difference* of a and b is defined as the *sum* of a and the *additive inverse* of b, and since R_n is closed under addition, it must also be closed under subtraction.

As examples, in R_7, $5 - 3 = 5 + (-3) = 5 + 4 = 2$, while $2 - 5 = 2 + (-5) = 2 + 2 = 4$. In R_{11}, $10 - 4 = 10 + (-4) = 10 + 7 = 6$, while $5 - 9 = 5 + (-9) = 5 + 2 = 7$. As exercises, construct subtraction tables for the elements of R_7 and R_{11}. Finally, how would the "clock" method of Section 13 be used to define the operation of subtraction?

PROBLEMS

14.1 Construct addition and multiplication tables for each of the systems R_4, R_9, R_{10}, and R_{12}.

14.2 Construct subtraction tables for each of the systems R_5 and R_8.

14.3 Compute each of the following expressions in R_7, R_{10}, and R_{12}.
(a) $5(4 - 6)$
(b) $(-3)(3 - 5) + 2(3 - 6)$
(c) $[(5 + 4)(3 + (-2))](2 - 6)$

14.4 State and prove the cancellation law for addition in R_n for any positive integer n greater than 1.

14.5 Find $a + b$, $a - b$, and $a \times b$ for each of the following elements in the given systems.

(a) $a = 7, b = 5$, in R_9 and R_{11}
(b) $a = 11, b = 13$, in R_{15} and R_{17}
(c) $a = 12, b = 13$, in R_{15} and R_{19}
(d) $a = 37, b = 41$, in R_{47} and R_{59}
(e) $a = 22, b = 14$, in R_{33} and R_{55}

14.6 **(a)** If possible, compute each of the following expressions in R_7, R_8, R_{10}, R_{11}, R_{12}, and R_{13} : $\sqrt{3}$, $\sqrt{4}$, $\sqrt{5}$, $\sqrt{6}$, $\sqrt[3]{3}$, $\sqrt[3]{4}$, $\sqrt[3]{5}$, and $\sqrt[3]{6}$ (see Problems 13.10 and 13.11).

(b) Construct square root and cube root tables for each of the systems R_5, R_7, R_{10}, R_{11}, and R_{12} .

(c) Compute $\sqrt{1}$ and $\sqrt{-1}$ in R_5, R_7, R_{10}, R_{11}, and R_{12} .

14.7 *Fermat's Last Theorem* We know that each of the equations $x + y = z$ and $x^2 + y^2 = z^2$ has *infinitely many* solutions for positive integers x, y, and z. For example, $x = a, y = 2a, z = 3a$ is a solution to $x + y = z$ for *every* positive integer a, while $x = 3a, y = 4a, z = 5a$ is a solution to $x^2 + y^2 = z^2$ for *every* positive integer a. However, in 1637 a famous French mathematician, Pierre de Fermat, stated *without proof* that *for every integer* k > *2, the equation* $x^k + y^k = z^k$ *has no solutions in which* x, y, *and* z *are positive integers.* This conjecture has confounded mathematicians ever since then. It has never been proved as a general statement, but with the aid of electronic computers, it has recently been shown that there are *no* solutions in the positive integers for all values of k where $2 < k < 25000$. Most experts *feel* that the conjecture is valid for *all* $k > 2$, but a general proof still seems to be out of reach.

At this point, we would like to put Fermat's Last Theorem into the context of our R_n systems. We shall consider *only* solutions in which x, y, and z are *nonzero* elements in R_n .

(a) Show that the conjecture is false for every integer $k > 2$ in the system R_8 ; i.e., for each integer $k > 2$, exhibit solutions to the equation $x^k + y^k = z^k$ where x, y, and z are nonzero elements in R_8 .

(b) Show that the conjecture is false for every integer $k > 2$ in the system R_{12} .

14.8* Show that if n is a multiple of 4, Fermat's Last Theorem is false in R_n for every integer $k > 2$; i.e., for each integer $k > 2$, exhibit solutions to the equation $x^k + y^k = z^k$ where x, y, and z are nonzero elements in R_n (Appendix).

14.9 **(a)** Show that $x^2 + y^2 = z^2$ has *no* solutions in which x, y, and z are nonzero elements in R_5 .

(b) Show that $x^3 + y^3 = z^3$ has exactly 12 solutions in which x, y, and z are nonzero elements in R_5 .

(c) Compare the results of (a) and (b) with Fermat's Last Theorem.

14.10* **(a)** Show that in R_5, if k is any positive *even* integer, $x^k + y^k = z^k$ has *no* solutions in which x, y, and z are nonzero elements of R_5 .

(b) Show that in R_5, if k is any positive *odd* integer, $x^k + y^k = z^k$ has exactly 12 solutions in which x, y, and z are nonzero elements of R_5 .

(c) Compare the results of (a) and (b) with Fermat's Last Theorem.

Section *15*

MULTIPLICATIVE INVERSES IN R$_n$

An element a'' in R_n is the *multiplicative inverse* of an element a in R_n if $a \times a'' = 1$. We denote the multiplicative inverse of a by $1/a$. If the student consults the multiplication tables for R_7 and R_5, he will see that, in each of these systems, *every* nonzero element has a multiplicative inverse. However, if the multiplication tables for R_6 and R_8 are consulted, the elements 2, 3, and 4 in R_6 and the elements 2, 4, and 6 in R_8 are seen to possess no multiplicative inverse. Consequently, we need a criterion that will enable us to tell whether a nonzero element a in R_n has a multiplicative inverse in R_n, and we also need a method for computing this inverse when it exists.

We use a special case of the following result mentioned in Theorem 5.2: if $(a, b) = d$, we can always find integers x and y such that $ax + by = d$. We also use the technique explained in the proof of Theorem 5.2 for finding the integers x and y. For example, let us find $1/11$ in R_{13}. Now, $(11, 13) = 1$ and Theorem 5.2 tells us that there are integers x and y in Z such that $11x + 13y = 1$. Using the technique mentioned in the proof of Theorem 5.2, we proceed to find x and y by first dividing 13 by 11, obtaining $13 = 1 \cdot 11 + 2$; we then divide 11 by 2, obtaining $11 = 5 \cdot 2 + 1$. It follows that $13 - 1 \cdot 11 = 2$ and $11 - 5 \cdot 2 = 11 - 5(13 - 1 \cdot 11) = 6 \cdot 11 + (-5)(13) = 1$. Therefore, $x = 6$ and $y = -5$. Now, $11 \cdot 6 = 1 + 5 \cdot 13$; hence, on dividing $11 \cdot 6$ by 13, we obtain the remainder 1. Therefore, $11 \cdot 6 = 1$ in R_{13} and so $1/11 = 6$ in R_{13}.

Now, in general, if we let a be a member of R_n, $b = n$, and $d = 1$, we have by Theorem 5.3 that whenever an element a in R_n is relatively prime to n, there exist integers x and y in Z such that $ax + ny = 1$. Then, $ax = 1 + (-y)n$, and thus the product ax in Z yields the remainder 1 when it is divided by n. Therefore, $ax = 1$ in R_n. Now, if $1 \leq x \leq n - 1$, then $x = 1/a$ in R_n. However, if $x < 1$ or $x > n - 1$, we simply divide x by n and take the remainder x' as the element of R_n that equals $1/a$. For example, in R_7 we may obtain $1/5$ from any one of the following equations: $5 \cdot 3 + 7(-2) = 1$, $5 \cdot 10 + 7(-7) = 1$, and $5(-4) + 7 \cdot 3 = 1$. In the first equation, $x = 3$ gives the inverse directly. In the second equation, $x = 10$ is divided by 7, yielding $x' = 3$ as the remainder. Finally, in the third equation, $x = -4$ may be divided by 7, yielding $-4 = (-1)(7) + 3$ and the remainder $x' = 3$ again. In the *last* case, however, we could have observed that in R_7, -4 is precisely $7 - 4 = 3$, and thus we could have obtained the answer directly. Therefore, our criterion is stated as follows.

15.1 Theorem   An element a in R_n has a *multiplicative inverse* if $(a, n) = 1$.

The *converse* of the preceding theorem is also true, i.e., if $1/a$ exists in R_n, then $(a, n) = 1$. The student should try to prove this as an exercise. (*Hint.* Show that if $1/a$ exists in R_n, there are integers r and s in Z such that $ar + ns = 1$. Then apply Theorem 5.3(B).)

Corollary   In R_p, where p is a prime, *every nonzero element* has a *multiplicative inverse*.

The proof follows from the fact that if p is a prime and $1 \leq a < p$, then $(a, p) = 1$ and we may apply the preceding theorem.

EXAMPLES

1. Find $1/15$: (a) in R_{31} and (b) in R_{47}.
    (a) $31 = 2(15) + 1$; therefore, $(15)(-2) = 1 + (31)(-1)$ and $(15)(-2)$ in Z has remainder 1 on division by 31. Consequently, $(15)(-2) = 1$ in R_{31} and, since $-2 = 29$, we have $1/15 = 29$ in R_{31}.
    (b) $47 = 3(15) + 2$ and $15 = 7 \cdot 2 + 1$; therefore, $15 - 7 \cdot 2 = 15 - 7(47 - 3(15)) = (15)(22) - 7(47) = 1$. Hence, $(15)(22) = 1 + 7(47)$ and $(15)(22)$ in Z has remainder 1 on division by 47. Consequently, $(15)(22) = 1$ in R_{47} and so $1/15 = 22$ in R_{47}.
2. In R_{12}, find $1/7$.

$$12 = 1 \cdot 7 + 5 \ (5 = 12 - 1 \cdot 7)$$
$$7 = 1 \cdot 5 + 2 \ (2 = 7 - 1 \cdot 5)$$
$$5 = 2 \cdot 2 + 1 \ (1 = 5 - 2 \cdot 2)$$

MULTIPLICATIVE INVERSES IN R_n   75

Substituting for 5 and 2 in the last equation, we obtain

$$(12 - 1 \cdot 7) - 2(7 - 1 \cdot (12 - 1 \cdot 7)) = 3 \cdot 12 + (-5)7 = 1 \,.$$

Therefore, $7(-5) = 1 + (-3)(12)$, and so $7(-5)$ in Z has remainder 1 on division by 12. But $-5 = 7$ in R_{12}; therefore, $1/7 = 7$ in R_{12}.

3. In R_{59}, find $1/27$.

$$59 = 2(27) + 5 \; (5 = 59 - 2(27))$$
$$27 = 5 \cdot 5 + 2 \; (2 = 27 - 5 \cdot 5)$$
$$5 = 2 \cdot 2 + 1 \; (1 = 5 - 2 \cdot 2)$$

Now, $5 - 2 \cdot 2 = (59 - 2(27)) - 2[27 - 5(59 - 2(27))] = (11)(59) + (-24)(27) = 1$. Therefore, $(27)(-24) = 1 + (-11)(59)$ and, since $-24 = 35$ in R_{59}, $1/27 = 35$ in R_{59}.

DIVISION IN R_n

We just saw that in R_n, if an element a is relatively prime to n, then the multiplicative inverse of a, denoted by $1/a$, exists. Now, we define the operation of *division* in R_n in the following way: for any two elements a and b in R_n, $b \div a = (b)(1/a)$ *provided* $1/a$ exists in R_n. Therefore, the quotient b/a is defined in R_n whenever the multiplicative inverse of the denominator exists in R_n. Note that this definition of division *differs* from the one given for integers in Section 1. In fact, this is a *stronger* definition, since it demands the existence of the multiplicative inverse of the divisor while the one in Section 1 does not.

Now, in R_p where p is a prime, every nonzero element a has a multiplicative inverse. Therefore, as a consequence of our definition of division, b/a exists in R_p for any element b and any nonzero element a. Therefore, R_p is *closed* under nonzero division.

As examples, in R_7, $2/5 = 2(1/5) = 2 \cdot 3 = 6$ while $5/3 = 5(1/3) = 5 \cdot 5 = 4$; in R_{11}, $2/7 = 2(1/7) = 2 \cdot 8 = 5$ while $5/9 = 5(1/9) = 5 \cdot 5 = 3$; in R_8, $2/5 = 2(1/5) = 2 \cdot 5 = 2$, while $5/2$ *does not exist*, since 2 does *not* possess a multiplicative inverse in R_8.

Also, in R_8, do not be tempted to say $4/2 = 2$ because $2 \cdot 2 = 4$ (this would be the case if we used a definition of division like the one in Section 1). According to our definition of division, $4/2 = 4(1/2)$ which is *not defined*, since $1/2$ does not exist in R_8. In fact, in R_8, we also have $2 \cdot 6 = 4$, and this would seem to indicate that $4/2 = 6$ as well. Also, in R_{12}, one might suspect that even though $1/3$ does not exist, $6/3 = 2$. This is not true, however, since $6 = 3 \cdot 6$ and $6 = 3 \cdot 10$ would also indicate that $6/3 = 6$ and 10 as well. Consequently, in the R_n systems, whenever the denominator does *not* have a multiplicative inverse, the quotient is *not* defined. As exercises, construct division tables for the elements of R_7 and R_{11}.

PROBLEMS

15.1 If possible, compute each of the following expressions in R_8, R_9, R_{10}, R_{11}, and R_{12}:

(a) $\dfrac{6(4+5)}{5}$ (b) $\dfrac{5(4-6)}{7}$ (c) $\dfrac{7(5+3)}{2}$

15.2 If possible, compute each of the following expressions in (a) R_9, (b) R_{10}, (c) R_{11}, (d) R_{12}, and (e) R_{13}:

$$-7/5, \qquad 8/3, \qquad 3/8, \qquad 4/7, \qquad -3/5$$

15.3 Find the additive and multiplicative inverses of each of the nonzero elements in R_{11} and R_{13}.

15.4 If possible, find $b \div a$ for each of the following elements in the given systems.
(a) $b = 7$, $a = 5$, in R_9 and R_{11}
(b) $b = 11$, $a = 13$, in R_{15} and R_{17}
(c) $b = 12$, $a = 13$, in R_{15} and R_{19}
(d) $b = 37$, $a = 41$, in R_{47} and R_{59}
(e) $b = 22$, $a = 14$, in R_{33} and R_{55}
(f) $b = 20$, $a = 49$, in R_{139} and R_{161}

15.5 Which of the following elements has a multiplicative inverse in the given system (you need not compute the inverse)?
(a) 50 in R_{63} (b) 171 in R_{183} (c) 121 in R_{227}
(d) 1512 in R_{1728} (e) 6912 in R_{20101}

15.6 (a) Show that in R_7, if $ab = 0$, then $a = 0$ or $b = 0$.
(b) Show that in R_8, if $ab = 0$, neither factor may be 0.

15.7 (a) Show that in R_p where p is a prime, if $ab = 0$, then $a = 0$ or $b = 0$ (Appendix).
(b) Show that in R_m where m is not a prime, there always exist non-zero elements a and b such that $ab = 0$. Find such elements in R_9 and R_{12} (Appendix).

15.8 Show that the cancellation law for multiplication is valid in R_7 but not in R_8.

15.9 Show that the cancellation law for multiplication is valid in R_p where p is a prime.

15.10 In Section 1, we mention many laws that are satisfied by the set of integers. Which of these laws are also satisfied by the R_n systems for any positive integer n? Are there any laws that are satisfied by the R_n systems but not by the set of integers?

15.11 Repeat the preceding problem for the R_p systems where p is a prime.

15.12 *Definition* We say that $a \leq b$ in R_n if $a \leq b$ in Z.
(a) What is the greatest common divisor of 2 and 3 in each of the systems R_7, R_8, and R_{11}?

(b) What is the least common multiple of 2 and 3 in each of the systems R_7, R_8, and R_{11} ?

15.13 **(a)** What is the greatest common divisor of any two elements a and b in R_n ? (Appendix)

(b) What is the least common multiple of any two nonzero elements a and b in R_p where p is a prime? (Appendix)

(c) Does Theorem 6.1 remain valid in R_p where p is a prime? (Appendix)

15.14 **(a)** Find the sum of all of the elements in each of the systems R_5, R_7, R_9, R_{11}, R_{13}, R_{15} .

(b) Find the sum of all of the elements in each of the systems R_4, R_8, R_{10}, R_{12} .

(c) Prove that in R_n, where n is an odd integer, the sum of all the elements is 0.

(d) Prove that in R_n, where n is an even integer, the sum of all the elements is the element $n/2$.

15.15 **(a)** Find the product of all the nonzero elements in each of the systems R_6, R_8, R_9, R_{10} .

(b) Find the product of all the nonzero elements in each of the systems R_5, R_7, R_{11}, R_{13} .

(c) Prove that in R_n, where n is a composite integer greater than 4, the product of all the nonzero elements is 0. (*Hint.* See Problem 15.7(b).)

(d)* Prove that in R_p, where p = prime, the product of all the nonzero elements is $p - 1$ (Appendix).

15.16 *Definition* A number k in R_n is said to be a *perfect* number if the *sum* of *all* its *divisors* in R_n is equal to $2k$ in R_n .

(a) Find all the perfect numbers in each of the systems R_4, R_5, R_7, R_8, R_9, R_{11}, R_{12} .

(b) Is 6 a perfect number in either R_{13} or R_{14} ?

(c) Is 7 a perfect number in either R_{13} or R_{14} ?

(d) Is 28 a perfect number in either R_{33} or R_{56} ?

15.17 Prove that zero is the only perfect number in R_p where p is a prime. (*Hint.* Use the result given in Problem 15.14(c).)

15.18 *Definition* A number k in R_n is said to be *multiplicatively perfect* if the *product* of *all* its *divisors* in R_n equals k itself.

(a) Find all the *multiplicatively perfect* numbers in each of the systems R_n where n = 4, 5, 6, 7, 8, 9, 10, 11, 12.

(b) Is 16 a *multiplicatively perfect* number in either R_{17} or R_{19} ?

15.19 Prove that $p - 1$ is the only multiplicatively perfect number in R_p where p is a prime. (*Hint.* Use the result given in Problem 15.15(d).)

LINEAR AND QUADRATIC EQUATIONS IN R$_n$

The student may recall that the *general linear equation* in *one* variable x with ordinary integer coefficients is an equation of the form $ax + b = 0$ with $a \neq 0$, while the *general quadratic equation* in *one* variable x with ordinary integer coefficients is an equation of the form $ax^2 + bx + c = 0$ with $a \neq 0$. In the past, the student has probably had experience in solving both types of equations where the solutions for x were either integers or rational numbers. There might even have been instances when the solutions to a quadratic equation were *not* integers or rational numbers, but these will not come up in our work.

In this section, we give rules for solving linear and quadratic equations in the variable x with coefficients from the modular systems R_n. It turns out that the method of solution of the linear equations is quite simple and that, in dealing with the quadratic equations, we can often use the familiar formula for the roots of a quadratic equation. One of the purposes of this section is to present a brief "theory of equations" development for the modular systems. Another purpose is to exhibit the similarities between the methods of solving linear and quadratic equations over the integers and the methods of solving these same equations over the R_n systems. We begin with a theorem about *linear* equations over modular systems.

16.1 Theorem   Let a and b be any two elements in R_n with $a \neq 0$. The general linear equation $ax + b = 0$ has a unique solution if $1/a$ exists in R_n. The unique solution is given by $x = (-b)(1/a)$.

Proof Simply subtract b from both sides of $ax + b = 0$, obtaining $ax = -b$. Then solve for x by multiplying both sides by $1/a$, obtaining $x = (-b)(1/a)$ as the only possible solution.

Corollary In R_p, where p is a prime, the general linear equation $ax + b = 0$ always has a unique solution (since $1/a$ exists for every $a \neq 0$).

EXAMPLES

1. In R_7, $2x + 3 = 0$ implies $2x = -3 = 4$; therefore, $x = (1/2)4 = 4 \cdot 4 = 2$.

2. In R_{11}, $3x + 4 = 0$ implies $3x = -4 = 7$; therefore, $x = (1/3) \cdot 7 = 4 \cdot 7 = 6$.

3. In R_{12}, $5x + 4 = 0$ implies $5x = -4 = 8$; therefore, $x = (1/5) \cdot 8 = 5 \cdot 8 = 4$.

Examples where $1/a$ does *not* exist and either we do not obtain a solution or the solution is *not* unique.

4. In R_8, $2x + 6 = 0$ has two solutions $x = 1$ and $x = 5$, while $2x + 3 = 0$ has no solution.

5. In R_{12}, $4x + 4 = 0$ has four solutions $x = 2$, $x = 5$, $x = 8$, and $x = 11$, while $4x + 1 = 0$ has no solution.

QUADRATIC EQUATIONS IN R_n

If the student works out or looks up the proof of the formula for the roots of a quadratic equation $ax^2 + bx + c = 0$ where a, b, c are integers with $a \neq 0$, he will find that there are three important steps in the argument. They are:

1. A multiplication of the entire equation by $(1/a)$, reducing the leading coefficient to 1

2. A multiplication of the middle term by $(1/2)$ prior to "completing the square"

3. Taking the square root of the expression $b^2 - 4ac$.

Each of these three steps plays an important role in leading us to the familiar formula $x = \dfrac{-b \pm \sqrt{b^2 - 4ac}}{2a}$. Now, if a, b, c are elements in R_n with $a \neq 0$, this identical formula will give the roots of $ax^2 + bx + c = 0$ *provided* steps 1, 2, and 3 can be taken in R_n. Hence, the conventional quadratic formula can be applied in R_n if and only if

$(1/a)$, $(1/2)$, and the square root of $b^2 - 4ac$ *all exist* in R_n. But $(1/a)$ and $(1/2)$ exist in R_n if and only if both 2 and a are *relatively prime* to n (by Theorem 15.1). Hence, n must be *odd* and a must be relatively prime to n. Therefore, we may state the following result.

16.2 Theorem

If n is any *odd* positive integer, the general quadratic equation $ax^2 + bx + c = 0$ can be solved in R_n by the conventional quadratic formula if and only if $(a, n) = 1$ and $b^2 - 4ac$ has a square root in R_n.

Corollary In R_p where p is a prime greater than 2, the general quadratic equation $ax^2 + bx + c = 0$ has a solution if and only if $b^2 - 4ac$ has a square root in R_p (since $(a, p) = 1$ for every $a \neq 0$).

EXAMPLES

1. In R_9, solve $x^2 + 8x + 3 = 0$. Substituting in the quadratic formula, we obtain $x = \dfrac{-8 \pm \sqrt{1 - 4 \cdot 3}}{2} = \dfrac{1 \pm \sqrt{7}}{2} = \dfrac{1 \pm 4}{2}$.
Therefore, $x = (1/2)(5) = 5 \cdot 5 = 7$ and $x = (1/2)(-3) = 5 \cdot 6 = 3$.

As an exercise, substitute 7 and 3 into the original equation and verify that they do satisfy it. Also, prove that there are no other roots by substituting the remaining elements of R_9 into the equation and showing that each one fails to satisfy the equation.

2. In R_{15}, solve $7x^2 + 4x + 9 = 0$. $x = \dfrac{-4 \pm \sqrt{1 - 4 \cdot 7 \cdot 9}}{2 \cdot 7} =$
$\dfrac{11 \pm \sqrt{1 - 12}}{14} = \dfrac{11 \pm \sqrt{4}}{14} = \dfrac{11 \pm 2}{14}$. Therefore, $x = (1/14)(13)$
$= (14)(13) = 2$ and $x = (1/14)(9) = (14)(9) = 6$ are roots. But in R_{15}, $\sqrt{4}$ equals 7 as well as 2. Therefore, x is also equal to $\dfrac{11 \pm 7}{14}$, and so

$$x = (1/14)(3) = (14)(3) = 12 \quad \text{and}$$
$$x = (1/14)(4) = (14)(4) = 11.$$

As exercises, substitute each of the four roots into the original equation and show that each one does indeed satisfy the equation.

Finally, as a result of this example, we conclude that it is possible for a quadratic equation in certain R_n systems to have *more than* two roots, all of which are obtainable through the quadratic formula. Can a quadratic equation over the integers have more than two roots?

LINEAR AND QUADRATIC EQUATIONS IN R_n 81

3. In R_9, solve $3x^2 + 7x + 2 = 0$.

Since $1/3$ does not exist in R_9, we cannot use the quadratic formula to find the roots. The only recourse is to substitute each of the nine elements of R_9 into the equation and see which of them satisfy the equation. It turns out that only $x = 7$ is a root, and thus we have a quadratic equation with a single non-repeating root. Can this happen in a quadratic equation over the integers?

4. In R_8, solve $x^2 + 2x + 5 = 0$.

Since 8 is even, we cannot use the quadratic formula in this case either. If we substitute each of the elements of R_8 into the equation, we obtain $x = 1$ and $x = 5$ as roots.

5. In R_7, solve $x^2 + 2x + 4 = 0$.

$$x = \frac{-2 \pm \sqrt{4 - 4 \cdot 4}}{2} = \frac{5 \pm \sqrt{4 - 2}}{2} = \frac{5 \pm \sqrt{2}}{2} = \frac{5 \pm 3}{2}.$$

Therefore, $x = (1/2)(1) = 4$ and $x = (1/2)(2) = 1$ are the roots.

6. In R_7, solve $x^2 + 3x + 1 = 0$.

$$x = \frac{-3 \pm \sqrt{2 - 4}}{2} = \frac{4 \pm \sqrt{-2}}{2} = \frac{4 \pm \sqrt{5}}{2}. \text{ But } \sqrt{5} \text{ does not}$$

exist in R_7; hence, the equation has no roots in R_7.

7. In R_{13}, solve $x^2 + x + 1 = 0$.

$$x = \frac{-1 \pm \sqrt{1 - 4}}{2} = \frac{12 \pm \sqrt{-3}}{2} = \frac{12 \pm \sqrt{10}}{2} = \frac{12 \pm 6}{2}.$$

Therefore, $x = 9$ and $x = 3$ are the roots.

8. In R_{13}, solve $5x^2 + 3x + 7 = 0$.

$$x = \frac{-3 \pm \sqrt{9 - 4 \cdot 5 \cdot 7}}{2 \cdot 5} = \frac{10 \pm \sqrt{9 - 10}}{10} = \frac{10 \pm \sqrt{12}}{10}$$

$$= \frac{10 \pm 5}{10}.$$

Therefore, $x = (1/10)(2) = 4 \cdot 2 = 8$ and $x = (1/10)(5) = 4 \cdot 5 = 7$ are the roots.

FACTORIZATION OF QUADRATICS IN R_n

The student should recall that when he studied *quadratic* equations over the integers, he often factored them into *linear* factors. The general rule was that if the numbers u and v were roots of $ax^2 + bx + c = 0$, then $ax^2 + bx + c$ could be written, in factored form, as $a(x - u)(x - v)$.

For quadratic equations in the R_n systems, a similar rule holds. For instance, in the first example following Theorem 16.2, the roots of $x^2 + 8x + 3 = 0$ in R_9 are $x = 7$ and $x = 3$. Therefore, we may write

$x^2 + 8x + 3 = (x - 7)(x - 3)$ in R_9. As an exercise, multiply these factors and show that the product is equal to $x^2 + 8x + 3$ in R_9.

In Example 8, the roots of $5x^2 + 3x + 7 = 0$ in R_{13} are $x = 8$ and $x = 7$. Thus, we may write $5x^2 + 3x + 7$ as $5(x - 8)(x - 7)$ in R_{13}. As an exercise, multiply these factors and show that the product is equal to $5x^2 + 3x + 7$ in R_{13}.

However, in Example 3 following Theorem 16.2, something peculiar happens. The equation $3x^2 + 7x + 2 = 0$ has only *one* non-repeating root in R_9, yet $3x^2 + 7x + 2$ can be factored into $(3x + 1)(x - 7)$. In this case, the first factor does not give rise to a root in R_9; only the second factor does.

Finally, in Example 2 following Theorem 16.2, something even more peculiar happens. In this case, there are four roots and we end up with two distinct factorizations in R_{15}:

$$7x^2 + 4x + 9 = 7(x - 2)(x - 6) \quad \text{and}$$
$$7x^2 + 4x + 9 = 7(x - 12)(x - 11).$$

As exercises, multiply the factors in each factorization and show that each product equals $7x^2 + 4x + 9$ in R_{15}.

As a result of this example, we conclude that a quadratic equation can have *more than one* distinct factorization into linear factors in certain R_n systems. When you studied quadratic equations over the integers, did this ever happen?

As further exercises, find the factorizations of the quadratic equations given in Examples 4, 5, and 7 following Theorem 16.2.

We now give a summary of the various situations that can arise for a quadratic equation over an arbitrary R_n system.

(a) *No roots in R_n and no factorization into linear factors in R_n* (see Example 6).

(b) *No roots in R_n, but there is a factorization into linear factors in R_n.* For example, $4x^2 - 1 = 0$ over R_{12} factors into $(2x + 1)(2x - 1) = 0$. As an exercise, show that none of the elements in R_1 satisfies the equation.

(c) *One non-repeating root and a factorization into linear factors corresponding to it* (see Example 3 following Theorem 16.2).

(d) *Two roots and a corresponding factorization into linear factors* (see Examples 1, 4, 5, 7, and 8 following Theorem 16.2). Note also that in this case, the two roots may be equal (see Problem 16.16(e)).

(e) *More than two roots and more than one distinct factorization into linear factors in R_n* (see Example 2 following Theorem 16.2).

We conclude the section by stating, without proof, a theorem that should simplify the student's work in R_p systems where p is a prime.

16.3 Theorem For a quadratic equation over R_p where p is a prime, only situations (a) and (d) in the preceding summary can occur.

PROBLEMS

16.1 In R_7, solve each of the following equations:
 (a) $3x + 5 = 0$ (b) $2x - 5 = 0$ (c) $5x + 2 = 0$

16.2 In R_8, find all the solutions of each of the following equations:
 (a) $3x + 7 = 0$ (b) $2x + 6 = 0$ (c) $7x - 4 = 0$
 (d) $6x + 7 = 0$

16.3 In R_{11}, solve each of the following equations:
 (a) $7x + 8 = 0$ (b) $4x - 9 = 0$ (c) $6x + 5 = 0$

16.4 In R_{12}, find all the solutions of each of the following equations:
 (a) $2x - 4 = 0$ (b) $3x + 8 = 0$ (c) $5x + 7 = 0$
 (d) $7x - 11 = 0$

16.5 In R_{51}, find all the solutions of each of the following equations:
 (a) $5x + 7 = 0$ (b) $17x + 13 = 0$ (c) $33x + 11 = 0$
 (d) $10x - 17 = 0$

In Problems 16.6 through 16.10, find all the roots of the given equation in each of the systems indicated. Use the quadratic formula whenever possible.

16.6 $2x^2 + x + 2 = 0$, in R_3, R_5, and R_8

16.7 $x^2 + 3x + 1 = 0$, in R_5, R_7, and R_{11}

16.8 $3x^2 + 7x + 2 = 0$, in R_{10} and R_{12}

16.9 $x^2 + 5x + 8 = 0$, in R_{11} and R_{13}

16.10 $x^2 + 4x + 3 = 0$, in R_8 and R_9

16.11 Find all the roots of each of the following equations in R_{12}.
 (a) $5x^2 + 9x + 4 = 0$
 (b) $x^2 - 4 = 0$
 (c) $x^2 + 3x + 3 = 0$
 (d) $4x^2 + 4x = 0$

16.12 Using the quadratic formula, find all the roots of each of the following equations in R_{13}. Check the roots by substituting into the equations.
 (a) $x^2 + 2x + 4 = 0$
 (b) $x^2 + 11x + 10 = 0$

16.13 Find all the roots of the following equations in R_{15}. Use the quadratic formula whenever possible.
 (a) $x^2 + 12x + 5 = 0$
 (b) $5x^2 + 13x + 6 = 0$

16.14 Using the quadratic formula, find all the roots of the following equations in the given system. Check the roots by substituting into the equations.

(a) $4x^2 + 9x + 13 = 0$, in R_{17}

(b) $3x^2 + 13x + 1 = 0$, in R_{19}

16.15 By any means, find all the roots of each of the following equations in each of the given systems.

(a) $x^3 + 2x^2 + 2x + 1 = 0$, in R_7 and R_8 (Appendix)

(b) $x^3 + 7x^2 + 5x + 1 = 0$, in R_8 and R_{11}

(c) $x^4 + 3 = 0$, in R_7

(d) $x^4 + 5x^3 + 4x^2 + 2x + 1 = 0$, in R_7

16.16 Factor each of the following expressions into a product of linear factors if possible.

(a) $x^2 + x + 1$ in R_7

(b) $x^2 + 5x + 10$ in R_{17}

(c) $6x^2 + 5x + 4$ in R_9 (Appendix)

(d) $3x^2 + 4x + 5$ in R_{11}

(e) $x^2 + x - 4$ in R_{17}

(f) $3x^2 + 4x + 6$ in R_{15}

16.17 Factor each of the following expressions into a product of linear factors in at least *two* distinct ways.

(a) $x^2 + 7x + 2$ in R_{10} (Appendix)

(b) $x^2 + 7x + 6$ in R_{12}

(c) $3x^2 + 4x + 1$ in R_{15}

(d) $x^2 + 2x + 8$ in R_{16}

(e) $x^2 + 4x + 3$ in R_{21}

(f) $4x^2 + 4x$ in R_{12}

Section *17*

THE ALGEBRA OF 2 x 2 MATRICES

We shall study the 2×2 matrix algebra as an example of an algebraic system that satisfies many *but not all* of the basic laws of arithmetic that are satisfied by the integers and the modular systems. Although the elements of a matrix algebra are *not* integers or represented by integers, they are constructed by using integers, rational numbers, and also elements from the modular systems.

The general algebra of matrices appeared in 1858, and it has been an important scientific tool ever since. It first came up in connection with the study of transformations in plane geometry and we shall discuss this connection briefly later on. The early applications of matrices were mostly to problems in mathematics and physics. In later years, matrices were applied to problems in statistics, biology, chemistry, economics, and other fields. Unfortunately, most of these applications are beyond the scope of this text. Therefore, we will concentrate on the matrix algebra itself, and on the special elementary case of the 2×2 matrices in particular.

It turns out that the matrix algebra under addition and multiplication possesses all the fundamental properties that the integers and the R_n systems have *with the exception of the commutative law for multiplication*. At the time of its initial appearance in 1858, the matrix algebra was among the earliest known algebraic systems that satisfied all the basic laws of arithmetic *except* for the commutative law for multiplication. In fact, the first such system was discovered only in 1843. It was called the algebra of *quaternions*, and it was a clever extension of the system of complex numbers.

We now begin with some basic definitions in the algebra of 2×2 matrices.

Definition

A *2×2 matrix* is an array constructed from four numbers that are arranged in two rows and two columns and written in the form $\begin{pmatrix} a & b \\ c & d \end{pmatrix}$.

The letters a, b, c, and d represent numbers and are called the *entries* of the matrix. If these numbers are *integers*, we say that we have a *matrix over the integers*. If these numbers are *fractions* or *rational numbers* (see Problem 1.7), we say that the *matrix is over the rationals*. If these numbers are elements in an R_n system, we say that the *matrix is over* R_n.

Definition of Equality

We say that a matrix $\begin{pmatrix} a & b \\ c & d \end{pmatrix}$ equals a matrix $\begin{pmatrix} a' & b' \\ c' & d' \end{pmatrix}$ if and only if $a = a'$, $b = b'$, $c = c'$, and $d = d'$. Hence, two matrices are equal if and only if the entries in corresponding positions are equal.

Definition

If S is the set of all integers, or the set of all rationals, or the set R_n for some positive integer n, then the *algebra of 2×2 matrices over* S consists of the set of *all* 2×2 matrices with entries from S and we denote it by $M(S)$.

Note that if S is either the set of integers or the set of rationals, then $M(S)$ has *infinitely* many matrices. However, if $S = R_n$ for some positive integer n, then $M(S)$ has *finitely* many matrices. In fact, it has exactly n^4 distinct matrices, since any one of the n elements of R_n can fill any one of the four positions in the matrix, yielding $n \times n \times n \times n = n^4$ ways of constructing a 2×2 matrix over R_n.

ADDITION OF MATRICES

Definition

If $A = \begin{pmatrix} a & b \\ c & d \end{pmatrix}$ and $B = \begin{pmatrix} a' & b' \\ c' & d' \end{pmatrix}$, we define

$$A + B = \begin{pmatrix} a + a' & b + b' \\ c + c' & d + d' \end{pmatrix}.$$

Hence, we add two matrices by adding the corresponding entries position by position.

THE ALGEBRA OF 2×2 MATRICES
87

EXAMPLES

1. Over the integers: $\begin{pmatrix} 1 & 2 \\ 3 & 4 \end{pmatrix} + \begin{pmatrix} 0 & -1 \\ 2 & 3 \end{pmatrix} = \begin{pmatrix} 1 & 1 \\ 5 & 7 \end{pmatrix}$

2. Over the rationals: $\begin{pmatrix} 1 & 1/2 \\ -1/3 & 2 \end{pmatrix} + \begin{pmatrix} 1/5 & 7/8 \\ 3 & 1/4 \end{pmatrix} = \begin{pmatrix} 6/5 & 11/8 \\ 8/3 & 9/4 \end{pmatrix}$

3. Over R_5: $\begin{pmatrix} 0 & 1 \\ 2 & 3 \end{pmatrix} + \begin{pmatrix} 2 & 4 \\ 4 & 3 \end{pmatrix} = \begin{pmatrix} 2 & 0 \\ 1 & 1 \end{pmatrix}$

4. Over R_{13}: $\begin{pmatrix} 10 & 11 \\ 12 & 0 \end{pmatrix} + \begin{pmatrix} 2 & 3 \\ 5 & 7 \end{pmatrix} = \begin{pmatrix} 12 & 1 \\ 4 & 7 \end{pmatrix}$

If $A = \begin{pmatrix} a & b \\ c & d \end{pmatrix}$, $B = \begin{pmatrix} a' & b' \\ c' & d' \end{pmatrix}$, and $C = \begin{pmatrix} a'' & b'' \\ c'' & d'' \end{pmatrix}$ represent arbitrary matrices over the integers, or the rationals, or some R_n system, then the following *properties* hold for matrix *addition*. We leave the verifications to the student.

Closure Law $A + B$ is always a matrix.

Commutative Law $A + B = B + A$.

Associative Law $A + (B + C) = (A + B) + C$.

Identity element   The *zero* matrix $\begin{pmatrix} 0 & 0 \\ 0 & 0 \end{pmatrix}$, denoted by $\bar{0}$, possesses the property that $A + \bar{0} = \bar{0} + A = A$ for any matrix A (see Problem 17.15(a)).

Additive inverse   For each matrix $A = \begin{pmatrix} a & b \\ c & d \end{pmatrix}$, the matrix $\begin{pmatrix} -a & -b \\ -c & -d \end{pmatrix}$, denoted by $-A$, possesses the property that $A + (-A) = \bar{0}$ (see Problem 17.15(b)). Hence, the additive inverse of a matrix A is formed by the additive inverses of the entries in A.

Now that we have an additive inverse for each matrix, we may define the operation of *subtraction* in the algebra of matrices.

Definition

For any two matrices A and B, we define $A - B = A + (-B)$.

As exercises, subtract the matrices given earlier in Examples 1, 2, 3, and 4. Note that subtraction is defined in terms of addition; therefore, the set of matrices is certainly *closed* under the operation of subtraction. As exercises, show that the set of matrices under *subtraction* fails to satisfy the remaining properties that are satisfied under *addition*.

88   *SECTION 17*

After reading the definition of addition of matrices, you would expect the multiplication of matrices to be defined in such a way that corresponding entries are multiplied to obtain the product matrix, that is $\begin{pmatrix} a & b \\ c & d \end{pmatrix}\begin{pmatrix} a' & b' \\ c' & d' \end{pmatrix} = \begin{pmatrix} aa' & bb' \\ cc' & dd' \end{pmatrix}$. However, mathematicians find that *another* type of product is more valuable in the applications of matrices to mathematical problems. We shall give the definition of this product and then follow it with an example that may help the student to understand why we use this product instead of the simpler one in which the corresponding entries are multiplied.

Definition

Let $A = \begin{pmatrix} a & b \\ c & d \end{pmatrix}$ and $B = \begin{pmatrix} a' & b' \\ c' & d' \end{pmatrix}$ be any two matrices. We define the product $AB = \begin{pmatrix} aa' + bc' & ab' + bd' \\ ca' + dc' & cb' + dd' \end{pmatrix}$.

Note immediately that, under this definition, multiplication of matrices is *not* commutative in general, since, for arbitrary choices of the entries,

$$BA = \begin{pmatrix} a'a + b'c & a'b + b'd \\ c'a + d'c & c'b + d'd \end{pmatrix} \neq AB.$$

For example, if $A = \begin{pmatrix} 1 & 2 \\ -1 & 0 \end{pmatrix}$ and $B = \begin{pmatrix} 4 & 2 \\ 0 & -1 \end{pmatrix}$ are matrices over the integers, then $AB = \begin{pmatrix} 4 & 0 \\ -4 & -2 \end{pmatrix}$ and $BA = \begin{pmatrix} 2 & 8 \\ 1 & 0 \end{pmatrix}$. On the other hand, it is possible for two specific matrices to commute. For example, if $A = \begin{pmatrix} 2 & 1 \\ -1 & 0 \end{pmatrix}$ and $B = \begin{pmatrix} 3 & 2 \\ -2 & -1 \end{pmatrix}$ are matrices over the integers, then $AB = \begin{pmatrix} 4 & 3 \\ -3 & -2 \end{pmatrix} = BA$.

Note also that it is possible for the product of two nonzero matrices to be equal to the zero matrix. For example, if

$$A = \begin{pmatrix} 1 & 0 \\ 1 & 0 \end{pmatrix} \quad \text{and} \quad B = \begin{pmatrix} 0 & 0 \\ 1 & 1 \end{pmatrix}$$

are matrices over the integers *or* any R_n system, then $AB = \bar{0}$ with $A \neq \bar{0}$ and $B \neq \bar{0}$. Recall that in certain R_n systems we also obtained a zero product from two nonzero factors. For example, in R_6, $3 \cdot 4 = 0$ and $2 \cdot 3 = 0$. Consequently, the matrix algebra shares this property with certain R_n systems.

THE ALGEBRA OF 2 × 2 MATRICES   89

Observe that each entry of the product matrix is the *sum of the products obtained by multiplying a row of A by a column of B* according to the following rule:

product matrix entries	A	B
1st row, 1st column	= 1st row	× 1st column
1st row, 2nd column	= 1st row	× 2nd column
2nd row, 1st column	= 2nd row	× 1st column
2nd row, 2nd column	= 2nd row	× 2nd column

EXAMPLES

5. Over the integers: $\begin{pmatrix} 1 & -2 \\ 3 & -4 \end{pmatrix}\begin{pmatrix} 2 & 4 \\ -3 & 3 \end{pmatrix} = \begin{pmatrix} 8 & -2 \\ 18 & 0 \end{pmatrix}$

6. Over the rationals: $\begin{pmatrix} 1/2 & 1 \\ 3/2 & -2 \end{pmatrix}\begin{pmatrix} 0 & 1/2 \\ 1/4 & 1 \end{pmatrix} = \begin{pmatrix} 1/4 & 5/4 \\ -1/2 & -5/4 \end{pmatrix}$

7. Over R_7: $\begin{pmatrix} 1 & 3 \\ 5 & 1 \end{pmatrix}\begin{pmatrix} 4 & 6 \\ 3 & 2 \end{pmatrix} = \begin{pmatrix} 6 & 5 \\ 2 & 4 \end{pmatrix}$

As exercises, multiply the matrices given earlier in Examples 1 through 4.

If *A*, *B*, and *C* represent arbitrary matrices over the integers, or the rationals, or some R_n system, then the following three properties hold for matrix multiplication. We leave the verifications to the student as exercises.

Closure Law   *AB* is always a matrix.

Associative Law $A(BC) = (AB)C$.

Identity element   The *unit* matrix $\begin{pmatrix} 1 & 0 \\ 0 & 1 \end{pmatrix}$, denoted by *I*, satisfies the property that $AI = IA = A$ for any matrix *A* (see Problem 18.4(a)).

In general, an arbitrary nonzero matrix *may* or *may not* possess a *multiplicative inverse*, i.e., for a given matrix *A*, there may or may not be a matrix *B* satisfying the condition that $AB = BA = I$. Recall that in certain R_n systems, a nonzero element did not always possess a multiplicative inverse. Hence, we have another property that is shared by the matrix algebra with certain R_n systems.

As examples, we now exhibit some matrices over the integers. $\begin{pmatrix} 1 & 0 \\ 0 & 0 \end{pmatrix}$ does *not* have a multiplicative inverse. If it did, then there would be a matrix $\begin{pmatrix} x & z \\ y & w \end{pmatrix}$ such that $\begin{pmatrix} 1 & 0 \\ 0 & 0 \end{pmatrix}\begin{pmatrix} x & z \\ y & w \end{pmatrix} = \begin{pmatrix} x & z \\ 0 & 0 \end{pmatrix} = \begin{pmatrix} 1 & 0 \\ 0 & 1 \end{pmatrix}$. But this is impossible, since the second row, second column entry in the product matrix is *zero* for all values of x, y, z, and w, while the unit matrix has the integer 1 in that position. On the other hand, $\begin{pmatrix} 1 & 0 \\ 0 & -1 \end{pmatrix}$ is its own multiplicative inverse, while $\begin{pmatrix} 2 & 1 \\ 1 & 1 \end{pmatrix}$ has its multiplicative inverse equal to $\begin{pmatrix} 1 & -1 \\ -1 & 2 \end{pmatrix}$. When the multiplicative inverse of a matrix A exists, we denote it by A^{-1}. Hence,

$$\begin{pmatrix} 1 & 0 \\ 0 & -1 \end{pmatrix}^{-1} = \begin{pmatrix} 1 & 0 \\ 0 & -1 \end{pmatrix} \quad \text{and} \quad \begin{pmatrix} 2 & 1 \\ 1 & 1 \end{pmatrix}^{-1} = \begin{pmatrix} 1 & -1 \\ -1 & 2 \end{pmatrix}.$$

Finally, the *distributive laws* for multiplication with respect to addition are satisfied, that is, $A(B + C) = AB + AC$ and $(B + C)A = BA + CA$ for any three matrices A, B, and C. We again leave the verification as an exercise for the student. Note that we state *two* distributive laws because of the non-commutativity of matrix multiplication. The first one is called the *left-hand distributive law* and the second one is called the *right-hand distributive law*.

FURTHER EXPLANATION OF MATRIX MULTIPLICATION

We conclude this section with a brief discussion that partially explains the definition given for matrix multiplication. The discussion contains an example that demands from the student only a minimal background in plane geometry. Since this type of example has historical importance in the development of the theory of matrices, it should be of interest to the student. The problems that follow this section do *not* require an understanding of the example.

In geometry, a transformation of the plane is defined by a pair of linear equations in x and y. The pair of linear equations corresponds to a particular matrix that represents the transformation. When two transformations are applied successively, the corresponding matrices are *multiplied according to our definition* to obtain the matrix corresponding to the *composition* of the two transformations. For example, the following equations define a transformation of the plane in such a way that each point (x, y) is transformed into the point (x', y') where

$$x' = 2x + y$$
$$y' = x - y.$$

The matrix corresponding to this transformation is formed from the coefficients of x and y and is given by $\begin{pmatrix} 2 & 1 \\ 1 & -1 \end{pmatrix}$. Now, if (x', y') is transformed by a second transformation into a point (x'', y'') where

$$x'' = x' - y'$$
$$y'' = x' + y',$$

the corresponding matrix is $\begin{pmatrix} 1 & -1 \\ 1 & 1 \end{pmatrix}$. Applying both transformations successively, we obtain their composition under which a point (x, y) is transformed into a point (x'', y'') where

$$x'' = x' - y' = 2x + y - x + y = x + 2y$$
$$y'' = x' + y' = 2x + y + x - y = 3x + 0y.$$

The matrix corresponding to the composition is $\begin{pmatrix} 1 & 2 \\ 3 & 0 \end{pmatrix}$, which is precisely equal to the *product* of the other two matrices, the product being taken in the order $\begin{pmatrix} 1 & -1 \\ 1 & 1 \end{pmatrix}\begin{pmatrix} 2 & 1 \\ 1 & -1 \end{pmatrix}$.

As an exercise, repeat the preceding discussion using the following transformations:

$$x' = x - 2y$$
$$y' = x + y.$$
$$x'' = 2x' + 3y'$$
$$y'' = x' - y'.$$

PROBLEMS

17.1 Add each of the following pairs of matrices over the integers.

(a) $\begin{pmatrix} 1 & 5 \\ 2 & -4 \end{pmatrix}$, $\begin{pmatrix} 3 & -2 \\ 1 & 0 \end{pmatrix}$

(b) $\begin{pmatrix} -3 & 0 \\ 2 & 4 \end{pmatrix}$, $\begin{pmatrix} 6 & -2 \\ 3 & 1 \end{pmatrix}$

(c) $\begin{pmatrix} -5 & 2 \\ 3 & 1 \end{pmatrix}$, $\begin{pmatrix} 4 & 3 \\ -1 & 2 \end{pmatrix}$

17.2 Repeat Problem 17.1 considering the matrices to be over R_7.

17.3 Repeat Problem 17.1 considering the matrices to be over R_{13}.

17.4 Find the *additive* inverse of each of the six matrices given in Problem 17.1. Then subtract the second one from the first one in each pair.

17.5 Find the *additive* inverse of each of the six matrices given in Problem 17.1 considering them as matrices over R_7. Then subtract the second one from the first one in each pair.

17.6 Find the *additive* inverse of each of the six matrices given in Problem 17.1 considering them as matrices over R_{13}. Then subtract the second one from the first one in each pair.

17.7 Multiply each pair of matrices given in Problem 17.1.

17.8 Multiply each pair of matrices given in Problem 17.1 considering them as matrices over
    (a) R_7 **(b)** R_{13}

17.9 Multiply each pair of matrices given in Problem 17.1 considering them as matrices over
    (a) R_{11} **(b)** R_8

17.10 Suppose matrix multiplication is defined as

$$\begin{pmatrix} a & b \\ c & d \end{pmatrix} \begin{pmatrix} a' & b' \\ c' & d' \end{pmatrix} = \begin{pmatrix} aa' & bb' \\ cc' & dd' \end{pmatrix},$$

where all the entries are rational numbers. Answer each of the following questions.
    (a) Is the commutative law satisfied?
    (b) Is there an identity element?
    (c) Under what conditions does a matrix A have a multiplicative inverse?
    (d) Is it possible that $AB = \begin{pmatrix} 0 & 0 \\ 0 & 0 \end{pmatrix}$ without either A or B being the zero matrix?

17.11 Find a nonzero matrix A over the integers with the property that $A^2 = \begin{pmatrix} 0 & 0 \\ 0 & 0 \end{pmatrix}$.

17.12 Find a matrix A over the rationals, $A \ne \begin{pmatrix} 0 & 0 \\ 0 & 0 \end{pmatrix}$ or $\begin{pmatrix} 1 & 0 \\ 0 & 1 \end{pmatrix}$, with the property that $A^n = A$ for every positive integer n.

17.13 Let $A = \begin{pmatrix} 0 & -1 \\ 1 & 0 \end{pmatrix}$ be a matrix over the integers. Find the least positive integer k having the property that $A^k = \begin{pmatrix} 1 & 0 \\ 0 & 1 \end{pmatrix}$.

17.14 Let $A = \begin{pmatrix} 1 & 1 \\ 1 & 1 \end{pmatrix}$ be a matrix (a) over the integers and (b) over R_2. For any positive integer $n > 1$, find A^n.

17.15 Let $A = \begin{pmatrix} a & b \\ c & d \end{pmatrix}$, $B = \begin{pmatrix} x & y \\ z & w \end{pmatrix}$, and $C = \begin{pmatrix} r & s \\ t & u \end{pmatrix}$ be matrices over the integers.
    (a) Prove that if $A + B = A$, then $B = \begin{pmatrix} 0 & 0 \\ 0 & 0 \end{pmatrix}$ (Appendix).
    (b) Prove that if $A + C = \begin{pmatrix} 0 & 0 \\ 0 & 0 \end{pmatrix}$, then $C = \begin{pmatrix} -a & -b \\ -c & -d \end{pmatrix}$ (Appendix).

Section *18*

THE MULTIPLICATIVE INVERSE OF A 2 x 2 MATRIX

In this section, we give a condition for the existence of the multiplicative inverse of an arbitrary 2×2 matrix. A technique is also discussed for finding the multiplicative inverse when it exists and a formula is derived for it.

The problem is approached in the following way. We assume that a matrix A has a multiplicative inverse and then we study the consequences of this assumption. This approach eventually culminates in the derivation of the formula for the multiplicative inverse.

Let $A = \begin{pmatrix} a & b \\ c & d \end{pmatrix}$ be any 2×2 matrix over the rationals. If A has a multiplicative inverse with $A^{-1} = \begin{pmatrix} x & z \\ y & w \end{pmatrix}$, then $AA^{-1} = \begin{pmatrix} 1 & 0 \\ 0 & 1 \end{pmatrix}$, which is the Identity Matrix for multiplication. Hence,

$$AA^{-1} = \begin{pmatrix} a & b \\ c & d \end{pmatrix}\begin{pmatrix} x & z \\ y & w \end{pmatrix} = \begin{pmatrix} ax + by & az + bw \\ cx + dy & cz + dw \end{pmatrix} = \begin{pmatrix} 1 & 0 \\ 0 & 1 \end{pmatrix}.$$

Therefore, we obtain the following two pairs of linear equations which may be solved simultaneously, the first pair for x and y and the second pair for z and w:

$$ax + by = 1 \quad \text{and} \quad cx + dy = 0.$$
$$az + bw = 0 \quad \text{and} \quad cz + dw = 1.$$

To find the solution for the first pair, we multiply the first equation by d and the second equation by b, obtaining $adx + bdy = d$ and $bcx +$

$bdy = 0$. Subtracting the second equation from the first, the y terms cancel and we obtain $(ad - bc)x = d$. Now, if $ad - bc \neq 0$, we may solve for x, obtaining $x = \dfrac{d}{ad - bc}$. Substituting for x in the first equation, we have $ad\left(\dfrac{d}{ad - bc}\right) + bdy = d$. Isolating bdy, we obtain $bdy = d - ad\left(\dfrac{d}{ad - bc}\right) = \dfrac{d(ad - bc) - add}{ad - bc} = \dfrac{-bcd}{ad - bc}$. Now, if $bd \neq 0$, then we may solve for y, obtaining $y = \dfrac{-c}{ad - bc}$.

In a similar way, the student may solve the second pair of equations $az + bw = 0$ and $cz + dw = 1$, obtaining

$$z = \frac{-b}{ad - bc} \quad \text{and} \quad w = \frac{a}{ad - bc}.$$

Now, if $bd = 0$, then either b or d must be zero. They cannot both be zero, or else $ad - bc = 0$ and there is *no* solution, since we cannot divide by zero to obtain x, y, z, and w. As exercises, the student should show that when $b = 0$, the solutions are $x = 1/a$, $y = -c/ad$, $z = 0$, and $w = 1/d$, and when $d = 0$, the solutions are $x = 0$, $y = 1/b$, $z = 1/c$, and $w = a/-bc$.

Consequently, we may conclude that a matrix $A = \begin{pmatrix} a & b \\ c & d \end{pmatrix}$ over the rationals has a multiplicative inverse if and only if $ad - bc \neq 0$. If we let $\Delta = ad - bc$, we may write the matrix A^{-1} as $\begin{pmatrix} d/\Delta & -b/\Delta \\ -c/\Delta & a/\Delta \end{pmatrix}$. Δ is called the *determinant* of A.

Finally, comparing A with A^{-1}, we see that the multiplicative inverse of A may be obtained from A by going through the following three steps:

1. Switch the numbers in the main diagonal, obtaining $\begin{pmatrix} d & b \\ c & a \end{pmatrix}$

2. Multiply the numbers in the other diagonal by -1, obtaining $\begin{pmatrix} d & -b \\ -c & a \end{pmatrix}$

3. Multiply each of the four numbers in the matrix by $1/\Delta$ where $\Delta = ad - bc$, provided $\Delta \neq 0$.

Remark Observe that if the preceding discussion is applied to a matrix $A = \begin{pmatrix} a & b \\ c & d \end{pmatrix}$ where a, b, c, d are in R_n, we would obtain the same results, arriving at the same three-step rule for finding the multiplicative inverse of A. The only difference would be that the condition $\Delta = ad - bc \neq 0$ would be replaced by the condition $\Delta = ad - bc$ *has a multi-*

plicative inverse in R_n. Hence, a matrix over R_n has a multiplicative inverse if and only if its determinant Δ has a multiplicative inverse in R_n. Note that if $n = p$ where p is a prime, then the condition would remain $ad - bc \neq 0$ in R_p since every nonzero element in R_p has a multiplicative inverse.

EXAMPLES

1. Find the multiplicative inverse of the matrix $\begin{pmatrix} 2 & 1 \\ 4 & 3 \end{pmatrix}$ over the rationals. Now, $\Delta = 2 \cdot 3 - 1 \cdot 4 = 2 \neq 0$; therefore, the inverse exists. Switching the numbers in the main diagonal, we obtain $\begin{pmatrix} 3 & 1 \\ 4 & 2 \end{pmatrix}$. Multiplying the numbers in the other diagonal by -1, we have $\begin{pmatrix} 3 & -1 \\ -4 & 2 \end{pmatrix}$. Finally, we multiply each number in the matrix by $1/\Delta = 1/2$, obtaining the inverse matrix $\begin{pmatrix} 3/2 & -1/2 \\ -2 & 1 \end{pmatrix}$. Checking the answer, we take the product $\begin{pmatrix} 2 & 1 \\ 4 & 3 \end{pmatrix} \begin{pmatrix} 3/2 & -1/2 \\ -2 & 1 \end{pmatrix}$, obtaining $\begin{pmatrix} 1 & 0 \\ 0 & 1 \end{pmatrix}$.

2. Find the multiplicative inverse of the matrix $\begin{pmatrix} 1 & -2 \\ 3 & 2 \end{pmatrix}$ over the rationals. Since $\Delta = 1 \cdot 2 - (-2) \cdot 3 = 8$, the inverse exists. Switching the numbers in the main diagonal and multiplying the numbers in the other diagonal by -1, we obtain $\begin{pmatrix} 2 & 2 \\ -3 & 1 \end{pmatrix}$. Now, we multiply each number in the matrix by $1/\Delta = 1/8$, arriving at the inverse matrix

$$\begin{pmatrix} 1/4 & 1/4 \\ -3/8 & 1/8 \end{pmatrix}.$$

The student should check the answer by showing

$$\begin{pmatrix} 1 & -2 \\ 3 & 2 \end{pmatrix} \begin{pmatrix} 1/4 & 1/4 \\ -3/8 & 1/8 \end{pmatrix} = \begin{pmatrix} 1 & 0 \\ 0 & 1 \end{pmatrix}.$$

3. Find the multiplicative inverse of the matrix $\begin{pmatrix} 1 & -2 \\ 3 & 2 \end{pmatrix}$ where the matrix is over:

   (a) R_5 (b) R_7 (c) R_8 (d) R_9 (e) R_{12}.

(a) Over R_5, $\begin{pmatrix} 1 & -2 \\ 3 & 2 \end{pmatrix} = \begin{pmatrix} 1 & 3 \\ 3 & 2 \end{pmatrix}$ and $\Delta = 1 \cdot 2 - 3 \cdot 3 = 2 - 4 = 2 + 1 = 3$ with $1/\Delta = 1/3 = 2$ in R_5. Switching the numbers in the main diagonal and multiplying the numbers in the other diagonal by 4 (since $-1 = 4$ in R_5), we obtain $\begin{pmatrix} 2 & 2 \\ 2 & 1 \end{pmatrix}$. Finally, we multiply each number in the matrix by $1/\Delta = 2$, obtaining the inverse $\begin{pmatrix} 4 & 4 \\ 4 & 2 \end{pmatrix}$. The student should check the answer by showing that $\begin{pmatrix} 1 & 3 \\ 3 & 2 \end{pmatrix}\begin{pmatrix} 4 & 4 \\ 4 & 2 \end{pmatrix} = \begin{pmatrix} 1 & 0 \\ 0 & 1 \end{pmatrix}$ where the multiplication and the addition of the numbers are done in R_5.

(b) Over R_7, $\begin{pmatrix} 1 & -2 \\ 3 & 2 \end{pmatrix} = \begin{pmatrix} 1 & 5 \\ 3 & 2 \end{pmatrix}$ and $\Delta = 1 \cdot 2 - 5 \cdot 3 = 2 - 1 = 1$. Switching the numbers in the main diagonal and multiplying the numbers in the other diagonal by 6 (since $-1 = 6$ in R_7), we obtain $\begin{pmatrix} 2 & 2 \\ 4 & 1 \end{pmatrix}$. But $1/\Delta = 1$ and so this matrix *is* the inverse. Once again, the student should check the answer by showing that $\begin{pmatrix} 1 & 5 \\ 3 & 2 \end{pmatrix}\begin{pmatrix} 2 & 2 \\ 4 & 1 \end{pmatrix} = \begin{pmatrix} 1 & 0 \\ 0 & 1 \end{pmatrix}$ where the multiplication and the addition of the numbers are done in R_7.

(c) Over R_8, $\begin{pmatrix} 1 & -2 \\ 3 & 2 \end{pmatrix} = \begin{pmatrix} 1 & 6 \\ 3 & 2 \end{pmatrix}$ and $\Delta = 1 \cdot 2 - 6 \cdot 3 = 2 - 2 = 0$. Therefore, $1/\Delta$ does not exist in R_8 and thus the multiplicative inverse of the matrix does not exist.

(d) Over R_9, $\begin{pmatrix} 1 & -2 \\ 3 & 2 \end{pmatrix} = \begin{pmatrix} 1 & 7 \\ 3 & 2 \end{pmatrix}$ and $\Delta = 1 \cdot 2 - 7 \cdot 3 = 2 - 3 = 2 + 6 = 8$. Now, $1/8 = 8$ in R_9 and so the multiplicative inverse of the matrix exists. Using the three-step rule, we obtain $\begin{pmatrix} 7 & 7 \\ 3 & 8 \end{pmatrix}$ as the inverse. Once again the student should check the answer, doing the multiplication and the addition of the numbers in R_9.

(e) Over R_{12}, $\begin{pmatrix} 1 & -2 \\ 3 & 2 \end{pmatrix} = \begin{pmatrix} 1 & 10 \\ 3 & 2 \end{pmatrix}$ and $\Delta = 1 \cdot 2 - 10 \cdot 3 = 2 - 6 = 2 + 6 = 8$. But $1/8$ does not exist in R_{12}; therefore, the multiplicative inverse of the matrix does not exist.

Now that we know how to find the multiplicative inverse of a matrix when it exists, we may define the operation of *division* in the algebra of matrices.

Definition

If B is any matrix, and A is a matrix that has a multiplicative inverse denoted by A^{-1}, then we define $B \div A = BA^{-1}$.

For example, if $B = \begin{pmatrix} 1 & 0 \\ 0 & -1 \end{pmatrix}$ and $A = \begin{pmatrix} 2 & 1 \\ 1 & 1 \end{pmatrix}$,

then $B \div A = \begin{pmatrix} 1 & 0 \\ 0 & -1 \end{pmatrix}\begin{pmatrix} 1 & -1 \\ -1 & 2 \end{pmatrix} = \begin{pmatrix} 1 & -1 \\ 1 & -2 \end{pmatrix}$; if $B = \begin{pmatrix} 1 & 1 \\ 0 & 1 \end{pmatrix}$

and $A = \begin{pmatrix} 1 & 0 \\ 0 & -1 \end{pmatrix}$, then $B \div A = \begin{pmatrix} 1 & 1 \\ 0 & 1 \end{pmatrix}\begin{pmatrix} 1 & 0 \\ 0 & -1 \end{pmatrix} = \begin{pmatrix} 1 & -1 \\ 0 & -1 \end{pmatrix}$;

if $B = \begin{pmatrix} 1 & 2 \\ 4 & 3 \end{pmatrix}$ and $A = \begin{pmatrix} 1 & 0 \\ 0 & 0 \end{pmatrix}$, then $B \div A$ is not defined since A^{-1} does not exist.

Note that, in our definition of division, $B \div A$ was defined as BA^{-1} and *not* as $A^{-1}B$. Since there is no commutative law for multiplication of matrices, we cannot assume that $BA^{-1} = A^{-1}B$. Consequently, when $B \div A$ was defined, a choice had to be made between multiplying B on the left or on the right by A^{-1}. We decided to multiply B on the right by A^{-1} for *two* basic reasons. First of all, in the expression $B \div A$, we write A on the *right* of B, so it seems natural to multiply B on the *right* by A^{-1}. Secondly, the multiplication of B on the right by A^{-1} makes the definition of division of matrices closely resemble, in symbols, the definition of division we gave in the R_n systems. If you recall, in the R_n systems, the symbol $1/a$ was used for the multiplicative inverse of a, and we defined $b \div a$ to be $b(1/a)$. Hence, in symbols, we multiplied b *on the right* by the multiplicative inverse of a. Of course, in the R_n systems, there was a commutative law for multiplication, so it would have made no difference if we had written $b \div a = (1/a)b$. However, in the matrix algebra, it *did* make a difference. Consequently, a choice was made in such a way that the two definitions of division would resemble each other at least symbolically.

As an exercise, let $A = \begin{pmatrix} 2 & 1 \\ 4 & 3 \end{pmatrix}$, $B = \begin{pmatrix} 1 & -2 \\ 3 & 2 \end{pmatrix}$ (see Examples 1 and 2) and compute $A \div B$ and $B \div A$. As another exercise, let $A = \begin{pmatrix} 1 & -3 \\ 3 & 4 \end{pmatrix}$, $B = \begin{pmatrix} 1 & -2 \\ 3 & 2 \end{pmatrix}$ (see Example 3) be two matrices over (*a*) R_5 and (*b*) R_7 and compute $A \div B$ and $B \div A$.

PROBLEMS

18.1   Find the multiplicative inverse of each of the six matrices given in Problem 17.1 considering them as matrices over the rational numbers.

18.2   Repeat Problem 18.1 assuming that the matrices are over:
  (**a**) R_7 (**b**) R_{13}.

18.3   Consider each of the matrices given in Problem 17.1. Find the *additive* and *multiplicative* inverses of each of these matrices assuming that they are over:
  (**a**) R_{11} (**b**) R_8.

18.4*   Let $A = \begin{pmatrix} a & b \\ c & d \end{pmatrix}$, $I = \begin{pmatrix} r & s \\ t & u \end{pmatrix}$, and $B = \begin{pmatrix} x & z \\ y & w \end{pmatrix}$ be matrices over the rationals with $\Delta = ad - bc \neq 0$.

(a) Prove that if $AI = A$, then $I = \begin{pmatrix} 1 & 0 \\ 0 & 1 \end{pmatrix}$. (Appendix)

(b) Prove that if $AB = \begin{pmatrix} 1 & 0 \\ 0 & 1 \end{pmatrix}$, then $B = \begin{pmatrix} d/\Delta & -b/\Delta \\ -c/\Delta & a/\Delta \end{pmatrix}$.
(Appendix)

18.5 (a) List *all* the 2×2 matrices $\begin{pmatrix} a & b \\ c & d \end{pmatrix}$ where a, b, c, d are elements of $R_2 = \{0, 1\}$.

(b) List all the matrices in part (a) that have *multiplicative* inverses.

(c) Show that the set of matrices of part (b) is *closed under multiplication*.

18.6 Let $A = \begin{pmatrix} a & b \\ c & d \end{pmatrix}$ and $B = \begin{pmatrix} a' & b' \\ c' & d' \end{pmatrix}$ be any two matrices over the rational numbers.

(a) Show that the determinant of A *times* the determinant of B equals the determinant of the product AB.

(b) Show that the set of all matrices over the rationals having non-zero determinants is closed under multiplication but not under addition.

18.7 In parts (a), (b), and (c) of Problem 17.1, divide the first matrix by the second one, considering them as matrices over the rationals.

18.8 Repeat Problem 18.7 considering the matrices as being over
   (a) R_7 (b) R_{13} (c) R_8

18.9 Let $I = \begin{pmatrix} 1 & 0 \\ 0 & 1 \end{pmatrix}$, $A = \begin{pmatrix} 0 & 1 \\ -1 & 0 \end{pmatrix}$, $B = \begin{pmatrix} -1 & 0 \\ 0 & -1 \end{pmatrix}$, $C = \begin{pmatrix} 0 & -1 \\ 1 & 0 \end{pmatrix}$ be

matrices over the integers.

(a) Construct a multiplication table for the matrices I, A, B, C and use it to show that this set of matrices is closed under multiplication and satisfies the commutative law. Also, show that each matrix has a multiplicative inverse in the set and that this set is closed under division.

(b) Construct a multiplication table for the *nonzero* elements in R_5. Substitute I for 1, A for 2, B for 4, and C for 3 in the multiplication table for R_5 and compare the new table with the one that was constructed in part (a).

18.10 Let A be a matrix over the rationals. Suppose we define a *square root* of A, denoted by $\sqrt{A}$, as a matrix B with the property that $B^2 = A$. A matrix A over the rationals may have *no* square roots, *finitely many* square roots, or even *infinitely many* square roots. The student will see examples of each of these cases in the following problems.

(a) Let $A = \begin{pmatrix} 3 & 4 \\ -4 & 3 \end{pmatrix}$, $B = \begin{pmatrix} 2 & 1 \\ -1 & 2 \end{pmatrix}$. Show that $B = \sqrt{A}$.

(b) Let $A = \begin{pmatrix} 1 & 0 \\ 0 & 0 \end{pmatrix}$, $B = \begin{pmatrix} -1 & 0 \\ 0 & 0 \end{pmatrix}$. Show that $A = \sqrt{A}$, $B = \sqrt{A}$, and that these are the *only* square roots of the matrix A.

(c) Let $A = \begin{pmatrix} 0 & a \\ 0 & 0 \end{pmatrix}$ where a is *any* integer. Show that $A = \sqrt{0}$ where

$\bar{0}$ is the zero matrix $\begin{pmatrix} 0 & 0 \\ 0 & 0 \end{pmatrix}$, and that, as a consequence, the zero matrix has *infinitely many* square roots.

(d) Let $A = \begin{pmatrix} 0 & a \\ b & 0 \end{pmatrix}$ where a and b are *any* two rational numbers with $ab = 1$. Show that $A = \sqrt{I}$ where I is the *unit* matrix $\begin{pmatrix} 1 & 0 \\ 0 & 1 \end{pmatrix}$, and that, as a consequence, the unit matrix I also has *infinitely many* square roots.

(e) Let $A = \begin{pmatrix} 0 & a \\ b & 0 \end{pmatrix}$ where a and b are *any* two rational numbers with $ab = c$, and c is any nonzero integer. Show that $A = \sqrt{C}$ where $C = \begin{pmatrix} c & 0 \\ 0 & c \end{pmatrix}$, and that consequently the matrix C has *infinitely many* square roots.

III

PROBABILITY

INTRODUCTION TO PROBABILITY

We shall now study one of the most explosive branches of modern mathematics. Probability and its companion, statistics, have invaded almost every conceivable area of human endeavor, both scientific and non-scientific. Although a rigorous systematic development of the theory of probability has come about only in the twentieth century, the origins of the theory date back to the sixteenth and seventeenth centuries. In the beginning, mathematicians were concerned with applications of the theory to games of chance. In this section, we introduce you to the theory in a very natural way by using models that are based on certain elementary sampling problems. Many games of chance are just special cases of more sophisticated types of sampling problems. In the next section, we shall consider a variety of interesting models for problems that extend the theory into numerous modern areas. In later sections, many of our results are generalized and some remarkable conclusions will be drawn.

In order to have a general frame of reference in which we can discuss numerous types of models, we introduce the notion of an *experiment* that has a certain number of possible *results* or *outcomes*. We then proceed to some simple definitions and examples, and finally to some applications to sampling problems.

Suppose there is an experiment that has precisely *n* possible outcomes, each of them *equally likely* to occur. For example, the experiment of tossing a single die results in six possible outcomes, 1, 2, 3, 4, 5, and 6, each of them equally likely to occur; or the experiment of selecting a playing card at random from a standard deck of 52 cards results in 52 possible outcomes, each of them equally likely. We will deal almost exclusively with experiments that have equally likely outcomes, and we will call the set of all possible outcomes the SAMPLE SPACE of the experiment. If the sample space has *n* outcomes, we call each of them a *simple* outcome, and we assign to each one the *probability* $1/n$, thus reflecting the fact that they are *equally likely* outcomes. This assignment agrees with our intuitive idea of what the probability should be. For example, when tossing a single die, there are six numbers that could show up; hence, the probability that any particular one of the six numbers will show up should be $1/6$. This corresponds to our intuitive idea that there is *one chance in six* of a specific number appearing. Similarly, when selecting a playing card at random from a standard deck of 52 cards, we expect the probability that any specific card will be chosen to be $1/52$. This agrees with the intuitive notion that there is *one chance in fifty-two* of a particular card being picked.

Once we have an experiment, a sample space of *n* equally likely outcomes, and the probability $1/n$ assigned to each simple outcome, we can proceed to discuss the assignment of probabilities to *subsets* of outcomes in the sample space. For example, when tossing a single die, the set of *even* outcomes, 2, 4, and 6, is a subset of the sample space; the set of all *prime* outcomes, 2, 3, and 5, is a subset; finally, each simple outcome can be considered as a one-element subset of the sample space. When a card is selected from a standard deck of 52 cards, the set of all 13 simple outcomes that are spades is a subset of the sample space; the set of all aces is a subset consisting of 4 simple outcomes; and, once again, each one of the 52 cards can be considered as a one-element subset of the sample space.

In general, *subsets* of the sample space are called *events*. Hence, an *event* is any *subset* of outcomes in a sample space and may contain none, one, or more than one simple outcome. We assign probabilities to each subset or event in a sample space in the following manner: *if* S *is a sample space of* n *simple outcomes, and if* A *is a subset of* k *simple outcomes, the probability assigned to the event* A *is* k/n. We usually denote the *number* of simple outcomes in an event *A* by the symbol *N(A)* and the *probability* of the event *A* by the symbol *P(A)*. Hence, we write the formula for the probability of the event *A* in the following way: $P(A) = N(A)/N(S)$. For example, when tossing a single die, the probability of obtaining an even outcome is $3/6 = N(A)/N(S)$ where $A = \{2, 4, 6\}$ and $S = \{1, 2, 3, 4, 5, 6\}$; when we select a card from a standard deck, the probability of obtaining an ace is $4/52 = N(A)/N(S)$ where A is the set of all 4 aces and S is the set of all 52 cards.

Note that if A is any subset of the sample space S, then $0 \leq N(A) \leq N(S)$ and so $0 \leq P(A) \leq 1$. As an example of the extreme value 0, consider the probability of a 7 showing up on a toss of a single die. If A is the event a 7 shows up, then $N(A) = 0$ since 7 does not appear as an outcome in the sample space $S = \{1, 2, 3, 4, 5, 6\}$. Therefore, $P(A) = 0/6 = 0$. In general, whenever an event consists of *no* outcomes of the sample space S, the event corresponds to the subset of S consisting of *no* elements of S. This set is called the *empty subset* of S or simply the *null set*, and is denoted by the letter $\emptyset$. For example, when we select a card from a standard deck, the subset A of all outcomes consisting of the 11 of spades or the 12 of hearts is the null set. Hence, $P(A) = P(\emptyset) = 0/52 = 0$. Consequently, it is natural to assign a *zero* probability to the null set in *any* sample space.

On the other hand, if an event A consists of *all* the outcomes in a sample space S, then $A = S$ and $P(A) = P(S) = N(S)/N(S) = 1$. For example, the probability that a number greater than zero and less than 7 will show up in a toss of a single die is 1, while the probability of selecting a card from a standard deck that belongs to a red or black suit is also 1. Of course, from the practical point of view, we merely assign a *zero* probability to an event that *cannot* occur and we assign a probability of 1 to an event that *must* occur.

MORE DETAILED EXAMPLES

Suppose an experiment involves the selection of *one* card from a deck of ten cards numbered from 1 through 10. The sample space of outcomes is the set $S = \{1, 2, 3, 4, 5, 6, 7, 8, 9, 10\}$. Find the probability of each of the following events.

1. The event A of choosing a card with a prime number.
   Solution. Since $A = \{2, 3, 5, 7\}$, $P(A) = N(A)/N(S) = 4/10$.

2. The event B of choosing an even-numbered card.
   Solution. Since $B = \{2, 4, 6, 8, 10\}$, $P(B) = N(B)/N(S) = 5/10$.

3. The event C of choosing a card with a positive integer on it.
   Solution. The event C contains all the outcomes of S; therefore, $C = S$ and $P(C) = 1$.

4. The event D of selecting a card with a negative integer on it.
   Solution. Since no outcomes in S are negative integers, $D = \emptyset$ and $P(D) = 0$.

5. The event E of selecting a card with a number that is divisible by 3.
   Solution. Since $E = \{3, 6, 9\}$, $P(E) = 3/10$.

INTRODUCTION TO PROBABILITY

6. The event F of selecting a card with a number that is divisible by 5.
   Solution. Since $F = \{5, 10\}$, $P(F) = 2/10$.

7. The event G of choosing a card with a number that is a perfect square.
   Solution. Since $G = \{1, 4, 9\}$, we have $P(G) = 3/10$.

8. The event H of choosing a card with a number that is a perfect cube.
   Solution. Since $H = \{1, 8\}$, we obtain $P(H) = 2/10$.

In a more general type of problem, we choose *one* card from each of *two* sets R and T. For example, suppose a set R consists of four black cards numbered from 1 to 4, and a set T consists of three white cards numbered from 1 to 3. An experiment involving a choice of one card from each set has a sample space S consisting of 12 outcomes, since any one of the four cards from the set R can be chosen with any one of the three cards from the set T. The 12 outcomes of S can be denoted by 12 *ordered pairs* of numbers where the first number corresponds to the card selected from the set R, and the second number corresponds to the card selected from the set T. Thus, $S = \{(1, 1), (1, 2), (1, 3), (2, 1), (2, 2), (2, 3), (3, 1), (3, 2), (3, 3), (4, 1), (4, 2), (4, 3)\}$. In this problem, we ask questions of the following type.

1. Find the probability that the sum of the numbers on the cards selected is 5.
   Solution. The sum 5 results in each of the outcomes $(2, 3)$, $(3, 2)$, and $(4, 1)$. Therefore, the probability of selecting two cards with a sum of 5 is $3/12$.

2. Find the probability that only cards with odd numbers are selected.
   Solution. The outcomes with each card having an odd number are $(1, 1)$, $(1, 3)$, $(3, 1)$, and $(3, 3)$. Hence, the probability that only cards with odd numbers are selected is $4/12$.

As exercises, the student should determine each of the following probabilities.

3. The probability that only cards with even numbers are selected.

4. The probability that only cards with *distinct* numbers are chosen.

5. The probability that *at least one* card selected has an even number.

6. The probability that the *sum* of the numbers on the cards is 4.

7. The probability that the *product* of the numbers on the cards is 4.

8. The probability that the *product* of the numbers on the cards is 5.

9. The probability that the *sum* of the numbers on the cards is a number less than 8.

The preceding problem can be generalized to an experiment that involves the selection of *one* object from each of *m* sets, where *m* is *any* positive integer. In this case, if we have *m* sets $T_1, T_2, \ldots, T_m$, with $N(T_1) = k_1$, $N(T_2) = k_2, \ldots, N(T_m) = k_m$, then the sample space has $k_1 \cdot k_2 \ldots k_m$ outcomes. This follows from the fact that there are k_1 ways of selecting one object from T_1; $k_1 \cdot k_2$ ways of selecting an object from T_1 and one from T_2; $k_1 \cdot k_2 \cdot k_3$ ways of selecting an object from T_1, an object from T_2, and an object from T_3, and so on. For example, if a set T_1 has four numbered cards, a set T_2 has three numbered cards, and a set T_3 has two numbered cards, then the sample space S corresponding to the experiment that involves the selection of one card from each of the three sets has $4 \cdot 3 \cdot 2 = 24$ outcomes. As an exercise, list the 24 outcomes by using sequences of 3 numbers. For instance, (3, 1, 2) denotes the outcome corresponding to the selection of card number 3 from T_1, card number 1 from T_2, and card number 2 from T_3.

Note also that the sets $T_1, T_2, \ldots, T_m$ need not be distinct in order to apply the preceding results. For example, suppose a set T consists of 10 numbered cards and an experiment involves the selection of 3 cards from T, one at a time *with replacement* of each card after it is drawn. Then, each time we select a card, it comes from the set T, and we may apply our earlier results with $T = T_1 = T_2 = T_3$, obtaining a sample space of 1000 outcomes (10 possible on draw 1 *times* 10 possible on draw 2 *times* 10 possible on draw 3). However, if we select 3 cards, one at a time *without replacing* the drawn cards, we end up with a different sample space. Since the first card is drawn from T, we take $T = T_1$ with $N(T_1) = 10$. But the second card is drawn from a set T_2 that has only 9 cards (since the first card was *not* replaced). Finally, the third card is drawn from a set T_3, containing only 8 cards (since the first and second cards were *not* replaced). Consequently, in this case, the sample space has $N(T_1) \cdot N(T_2) \cdot N(T_3) = 10 \cdot 9 \cdot 8 = 720$ outcomes. In these situations, we solve problems like the following ones.

Suppose we select 3 cards *with replacement* from a deck of 10 numbered cards. Find the probability of each of the following events.

1. Only cards with even numbers are drawn.
   Solution. From the preceding discussion, the sample space has 1000 outcomes. The first card drawn can have an even number in 5 ways: 2, 4, 6, 8, and 10. Since we replace the first card, there are still 5 ways to draw an even-numbered card on each of the next two draws. Therefore, there are $5 \cdot 5 \cdot 5 = 125$ ways to select 3 even-numbered cards, so the probability is $125/1000 = 1/8$.

2. Only cards with prime numbers are drawn. We leave this solution as an exercise.

3. The cards are all distinct from one another. We also leave this solution as an exercise.

4. The cards drawn are in a consecutive ascending order.
   Solution. The first card drawn can be any one of the cards numbered 1, 2, 3, 4, 5, 6, 7, and 8. The second card *must* have a number equal to one plus the number on the first card and the third card *must* have a number equal to two plus the number on the first card. Therefore, the first card completely determines the second and third cards, and there are exactly 8 ways of selecting 3 cards in a consecutive ascending order. The probability is therefore $8/1000 = 1/125$.

5. Exactly two of the three cards have the same number. We leave this solution as an exercise.

Now, in the case where we select the 3 cards *without replacement* from a deck of 10 numbered cards, we *repeat* the preceding five problems. Recall that this sample space has $10 \cdot 9 \cdot 8 = 720$ outcomes.

Note that the probability that exactly two of the three cards have the same number (the fifth problem) is *zero* in this case, since no card can be drawn twice. In the first problem, there are still 5 ways of selecting an even-numbered card on the first draw; however, on the second draw, there are only 4 ways, and on the third draw, just 3 ways. Hence, we have $5 \cdot 4 \cdot 3 = 60$ ways of drawing 3 even-numbered cards, and the probability is $60/720 = 1/12$. We leave the second, third, and fourth problems as exercises.

In the problems that follow this section, you will find further applications of the preceding results.

PROBLEMS

19.1   A card is chosen from a deck of 12 cards, each one having a different month of the year written on it. Find the probability of choosing a card with a month that
(a) ends in y
(b) begins with j
(c) has 31 days
(d) has 30 days
(e) has less than 30 days
(f) has 5 letters
(g) has less than 5 letters
(h) has 8 letters
(i) has the letter u in it.

19.2   Suppose two cards are selected *without replacement* from the deck of cards mentioned in Problem 19.1. Find the probability that
   (a)   the cards represent months that are adjacent on the calendar
   (b)   both cards have a month which ends in y
   (c)   both cards have a month which begins with j
   (d)   both cards have a month which has 30 days
   (e)   both cards have a month with 5 letters.

19.3   A red die and a green die are tossed. List the 36 elements of the sample space as *ordered pairs* of integers and find the probability that
   (a)   the numbers showing have a sum 7
   (b)   the numbers showing have a sum 4
   (c)   the numbers showing have a product 12
   (d)   at least one number showing is a prime
   (e)   both numbers showing are primes
   (f)   both numbers showing are odd
   (g)   one number showing is odd, the other is even
   (h)   the product of the numbers showing is even
   (i)   the sum of the numbers showing is even.

19.4   Two cards are chosen one at a time *without replacement* from a standard deck of 52 cards. Find the probability that
   (a)   both cards are aces
   (b)   both cards are picture cards
   (c)   both cards are spades
   (d)   each card belongs to a different suit (Appendix).

19.5   Three cards are chosen one at a time *without replacement* from a standard deck of 52 cards. Find the probability that
   (a)   they are all aces
   (b)   they are all picture cards
   (c)   they are all spades
   (d)   each card belongs to a different suit.

19.6   Repeat Problem 19.4 *replacing* the card after each draw.

19.7   Repeat Problem 19.5 *replacing* the card after each draw.

19.8   In Figure 19.1, you will find a replica of the type of roulette wheel used at Monte Carlo. There are 37 positions on the wheel, with the numbers running from 0 through 36. Eighteen nonzero numbers are colored red and 18 black, with the 0 in green. The numbers from 1 through 36 are divided into odd and even numbers in the natural way. The number 0 is *not* considered to be odd or even. The numbers from 1 through 36 are further divided into *low* numbers (1 through 18) and *high* numbers (19 through 36). In the diagram, we have *shaded* the area of the black numbers, labeled the green area with a G, and left the area of the red numbers blank. Find the probability of each one of the following events coming up on *one* spin of the roulette wheel:
   (a)   the number 3
   (b)   an odd number
   (c)   a red number
   (d)   a high, odd number
   (e)   a low, red number
   (f)   a high, even, black number
   (g)   a low, odd, red number

(h) a positive multiple of 3
(i) a positive multiple of 5
(j) a prime
(k) a red prime
(l) an even, red multiple of 3
(m) a high, odd, black multiple of 5.

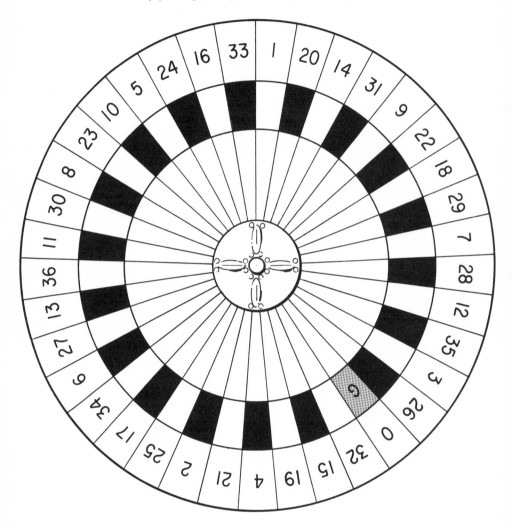

Figure 19.1

19.9 Using Figure 19.1 and the explanation given in the preceding problem, find the probability of each one of the following events coming up on *two* spins of the roulette wheel:

(a) two red numbers

    (b) two primes
    (c) one red and one black number
    (d) one high and one low number
    (e) two numbers that have a sum equal to 15
    (f) two numbers that have a product equal to 24.

19.10 Using Figure 19.1 and the explanation given in Problem 19.8, find the probability of each one of the following events coming up on *three* spins of the roulette wheel:
    (a) three red numbers
    (b) two red numbers and one black number
    (c) one red, one white, and one green number
    (d) three odd, black numbers
    (e) two odd numbers and one even number
    (f) three numbers that have a sum equal to 6
    (g) three numbers that have a product equal to 30
    (h) three numbers that have a product equal to 60.

Section 20

ADDITIONAL PROBLEMS IN PROBABILITY

In this section, we have selected a wide variety of problems, each one being a model for numerous others. Following the solution to each of them, we give examples of some interesting problems that can be solved by the technique exhibited in the solution to the model. Among the problems that follow the section, there are many that are related to the ones discussed in the text. We also introduce some new ones that require different techniques for their solution.

THE COUNTER PROBLEM

A counter is at the origin on a coordinate line (see Fig. 20.1). Suppose a coin is tossed and the counter is moved 1 unit to the right if a head results and 1 unit to the left if a tail results. Find the probability that (a) the counter is at the point 2 after 6 tosses of the coin, (b) the counter is at the point 1 after 8 tosses of the coin.

Solution (a)

The sample space is the set of all sequences of 6 jumps that the counter can make, where the jumps are made either to the left or right. For example, if the coin toss results in a head on the first, fourth, and fifth tosses, we can describe the corresponding sequence of jumps by (R, L, L, R, R, L) since the counter jumps right on the first, fourth, and fifth moves, and left on the other moves. In this case, the counter ends up at the origin after 6 tosses. If a head results only on the first and sixth tosses of the coin, we can describe the corresponding sequence of jumps by (R, L, L, L, L, R) and, in this instance, the counter ends up at the point -2. Finally, if 6 heads in a row result, we may describe the corresponding sequence of jumps by (R, R, R, R, R, R) and the counter now ends up at the point 6. In a similar fashion, each element in the sample space can be designated by a 6-term sequence of R's and L's. Now, each position in the sequence may be filled in one of two ways, an L or an R, and there are 6 positions to fill. Hence, there are $2 \times 2 \times 2 \times 2 \times 2 \times 2 = 2^6 = 64$ possible sequences and these represent all the elements of the sample space.

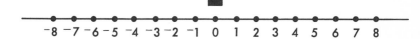

$$-8 \quad -7 \quad -6 \quad -5 \quad -4 \quad -3 \quad -2 \quad -1 \quad 0 \quad 1 \quad 2 \quad 3 \quad 4 \quad 5 \quad 6 \quad 7 \quad 8$$

Figure 20.1

Now, to find the probability that the counter ends up at the point 2 after 6 jumps, we must determine the total number of sequences in the sample space where the counter ends up at the point 2, and then divide by 64. These sequences all have one thing in common, namely, that the net difference between the number of R's and the number of L's appearing must be 2. This follows from the fact that the counter started at the origin and finished 2 units to the right of the origin. Now, let $r =$ the number of R's in a sequence and $f =$ the number of L's in a sequence. We then have, in any sequence where the counter ends up at the point 2, the following relations: $r + f = 6$ and $r - f = 2$. Adding the two equations and solving for r, we obtain $r = 4$. Therefore, $f = 2$ and every sequence where the counter finishes at the point 2 has precisely 4 R's and 2 L's. Now, the 2 L's can be placed in any of the following positions: 1 and 2, 1 and 3, 1 and 4, 1 and 5, 1 and 6, 2 and 3, 2 and 4, 2 and 5, 2 and 6, 3 and 4, 3 and 5, 3 and 6, 4 and 5, 4 and 6, 5 and 6. Therefore, a total of 15 different sequences can result when 2 L's and 4 R's are used. Consequently, the probability that the counter is at the point 2 after 6 tosses of the coin is $15/64$.

Solution (b)

We now wish to find the probability that the counter is at the point 1 after 8 tosses of the coin. Repeating the analysis given in the preceding solution, we find that the elements of this sample space may be represented by 8-term sequences of R's and L's and that there are $2^8 = 256$ such sequences. Let $r =$ the number of R's and $f =$ the number of L's in a sequence. Now we find that in any sequence where the counter ends up at the point 1 after 8 jumps, we have the following relations:

$r + f = 8$ and $r - f = 1$. Adding the equations, we obtain $2r = 9$, and so $r = 9/2$, which is *not* an integer. Therefore, *no* sequence in the entire sample space corresponds to the counter being at the point 1 after the eighth jump. Hence, the probability that the counter ends up at the point 1 after 8 jumps is zero.

We could also have described the counter problem in the following way. Two men, A and B, play a game in which a coin is tossed. If a head results, B pays A one dollar. If a tail results, A pays B one dollar. The counter is placed at the origin at the start of the game and it is used to keep score for A. When A wins one dollar, the counter is moved one unit to the right on the coordinate line. When A loses one dollar, the counter is moved one unit to the left. Then parts (a) and (b) in the original statement of the counter problem are equivalent to the following questions. Find the probability that (a) A has a net gain of two dollars after 6 tosses of the coin, (b) A has a net gain of one dollar after 8 tosses of the coin.

Finally, the counter problem is an example of what is called, in physics, a *random walk* problem. The general problem involves the haphazard movement of a particle along a straight line path.

THE ELEVATOR PROBLEM

Five people get on an elevator in the basement of a three-story building. Find the probability that (a) at least one person gets off on each floor, (b) the elevator is empty when it gets to the third floor.

Solution

Throughout this discussion, we assume that the people are *not distinguishable* from one another. Now the sample space is the set of all possible ways the 5 people can get off the elevator at floors 1, 2, and 3. We may designate the elements of this sample space by sequences of *three* numbers where the first number tells us how many people get off on the first floor, the second number tells us how many get off on the second floor, and the third number tells us how many get off on the third floor. For example, if 2 people get off on the first floor, 1 on the second, and 2 on the third, we use the sequence (2, 1, 2) to describe it. If 3 people get off on the second floor and 2 on the third floor, then we use the sequence (0, 3, 2) to describe it. Consequently, the sample space can be represented by the total number of distinct 3-term sequences (x, y, z) where $x \geq 0$, $y \geq 0$, $z \geq 0$, and $x + y + z = 5$. We will now list the 21 sequences which represent the sample space:
(5, 0, 0) (0, 5, 0) (0, 0, 5) (4, 1, 0) (4, 0, 1) (1, 4, 0) (0, 4, 1) (1, 0, 4) (0, 1, 4) (3, 2, 0) (2, 3, 0) (3, 0, 2) (2, 0, 3) (0, 3, 2) (0, 2, 3) (3, 1, 1) (1, 3, 1) (1, 1, 3) (2, 2, 1) (2, 1, 2) (1, 2, 2).

In part (a), we must determine the probability that at least one person gets off on each floor. This corresponds to counting the sequences that have no zeros, since a zero indicates that nobody gets off on a particular floor. There are only 6 such sequences. Therefore, the probability that at least one person gets off on each floor is $6/21 = 2/7$.

In part (b), we must determine the number of sequences that correspond to everybody getting off at floors 1 and 2. Since the elevator is empty when it gets to the third floor, we simply count the number of sequences having a zero in position 3; there are 6 such sequences. Therefore, the probability that the elevator is empty when it gets to the third floor is also $6/21 = 2/7$.

The elevator problem is an example of what is called, in physics, an *occupancy* problem. The general problem involves the *random* distribution of *indistinguishable* particles into *distinguishable* cells. This is the reason we assumed that the people were *not distinguishable* from each other. On the other hand, we assigned numbers 1, 2, and 3 to the floors in the building, since we were assuming that they *were* distinguishable from one another. There are other variations of the *occupancy* problem where the particles are distinguishable along with the cells, the particles are distinguishable but the cells are not, and neither the particles nor the cells are distinguishable.

Finally, by a *random* distribution of the particles into the cells, we mean that we also assume that each particle is just as likely to end up in one particular cell as it is in any other cell. Consequently, in the elevator problem we are really assuming that there is just as much of a chance that any one person gets off at floor 1 as there is that he gets off at either floor 2 or floor 3.

We now give some examples of problems that can be solved by imitating the solution to the elevator problem as we have described it.

Example 1 Five one hundred dollar bills are distributed among 3 students. Find the probability that (a) each student ends up with at least one hundred dollars, (b) the third student ends up with none of the one hundred dollar bills.

Example 2 Five baseballs are stored in 3 numbered boxes. Find the probability that (a) at least one baseball ends up in each box, (b) the third box is empty.

Example 3 Five automobile accidents occur over a 3-hour span of time. Find the probability that (a) at least one accident occurs during each of the 3 one-hour periods, (b) no accidents occur during the third one-hour period.

Example 4 Suppose we divide the year into 3 four-month periods as follows: January through April, May through August, and September through December. Suppose we select 5 students and ask them for the month of their birthday. Find the probability that (a) at least one student was born during each of the four-month periods, (b) none of the 5 students has a birthday in the four-month period from September through December.

Example 5 Suppose there are 5 misprints on the first 3 pages of a textbook. Find the probability that (a) there is at least one misprint on each of the 3 pages, (b) the third page has no misprints.

Example 6 Five bullets are fired into a target that is divided into 3 equal areas. Find the probability that (a) each of the 3 areas is struck by at least one bullet, (b) the third area is not struck by any of the 5 bullets.

As a final example, suppose two *white* dice are tossed. Let us assume that they are *two indistinguishable* particles being distributed into *six distinguishable* cells, one cell for each of the six digits that can appear on each die. For example, a 7 results if the dice fall into cells 1 and 6, or cells 2 and 5, or cells 3 and 4. A 4 results if the dice fall in cells 1 and 3, or if *both* dice fall in cell 2. The sample space is the total number of distributions of the two dice into the six cells. If the student makes a careful calculation, he will come up with exactly 21 such distributions. He will also find that, in this sample space, the probability that a 7 appears is $3/21 = 1/7$, while the probability that a 4 appears is $2/21$. Compare these answers with the ones obtained in Problems 19.3(a) and 19.3(b). As a further exercise in our new sample space, work out the probability that the product of the numbers appearing on the dice is 12, and compare your answer with the one obtained in Problem 19.3(c).

Now, before you jump to any conclusions because of the slight discrepancy between the answers, remember that there are *two different sample spaces* involved, the 36-element one of Problem 19.3 and the 21-element one we just discovered. Each answer is the *correct* answer for *its own* sample space. The amazing thing is that they *are* close to one another *despite the difference* in the sample space.

It turns out that mathematically *both* sample spaces are acceptable. In fact, the new one having 21 elements is perhaps a better reflection of reality than the old one having 36 elements. The reason for this is that, in most dice games, the two dice would have the same color and would thus be *indistinguishable* to the players.

THE CARD MATCHING PROBLEM

Suppose 4 red cards numbered 1 through 4 are spread out in a row in numerical order. A person has 4 white cards numbered 1 through 4. Suppose he shuffles the white cards and deals them out one at a time under the 4 red cards. Find the probability that the person obtains exactly (a) 4 matches, (b) 3 matches, (c) 2 matches, (d) 1 match, (e) no matches.

Solution

The sample space is the set of all possible ways that the 4 white cards can be dealt. The first card can be dealt in 4 ways, the second card in 3 ways, the third card in 2 ways, and the fourth card in only 1 way. Therefore, we have $4 \times 3 \times 2 \times 1 = 24$ different ways of dealing out the white cards. We may designate these 24 deals by using 4-term sequences with the numbers 1, 2, 3, 4 appearing in the order in which the corresponding white cards are dealt. For example, if card 2 is dealt first, card 4 second, card 1 third, and card 3 last, we use the sequence (2, 4, 1, 3) to describe this deal. The 24 sequences are: (1, 2, 3, 4) (1, 2, 4, 3) (1, 3, 2, 4) (1, 4, 2, 3) (1, 3, 4, 2) (1, 4, 3, 2) (4, 1, 2, 3) (3, 1, 4, 2) (4, 1, 3, 2) (2, 1, 3, 4) (2, 1, 4, 3) (3, 1, 2, 4) (2, 3, 1, 4) (2, 4, 1, 3) (3, 2, 1, 4) (4, 2, 1, 3) (3, 4, 1, 2) (4, 3, 1, 2) (2, 3, 4, 1) (2, 4, 3, 1) (3, 2, 4, 1) (4, 2, 3, 1) (3, 4, 2, 1) (4, 3, 2, 1).

Now, the red cards are in numerical order; therefore, a match results whenever a white card is dealt into a position that matches the number on the card. Hence, in terms of the sequences, a match occurs whenever a number in a sequence is equal to the number of the position in which it appears. For example, (4, 2, 3, 1) corresponds to a deal with 2 matches (in positions 2 and 3), (3, 1, 2, 4) corresponds to a deal with 1 match (in position 4), and (3, 4, 2, 1) corresponds to a deal with no matches since no number is the same as the number of its position.

Now, the sequence (1, 2, 3, 4) is the only one corresponding to 4 matches since *every* number is the same as the number of its position. Therefore, the probability of obtaining 4 matches is 1/24 and this is the answer to part (a). Since the 4 white cards are dealt one at a time, a match in 3 positions forces a match in the fourth position as well. Therefore, the probability of exactly 3 matches is *zero* and this is the answer to part (b). In part (c), we must count the sequences that correspond to 2 matches. There are 6 of them: (1, 2, 4, 3) (1, 3, 2, 4) (1, 4, 3, 2) (2, 1, 3, 4) (3, 2, 1, 4) (4, 2, 3, 1), and so the probability is 6/24. By counting the sequences that correspond to 1 match and no matches, the student will obtain the probabilities 8/24 and 9/24 as answers to parts (d) and (e), respectively.

The preceding problem belongs to a special class of problems in probability theory that are called *matching problems*. There are numerous examples of similar problems. We shall mention three of them and, for the sake of brevity, we shall include questions that relate only to parts (a) and (e) of the card matching problem.

Example 1   Four men enter a restaurant and check their hats. Upon leaving, the four hats become mixed up and they are returned to the men in a random fashion. Find the probability that (a) each man receives his own hat, (e) none of the men receives his own hat.

Example 2   A forgetful waiter brings four different dinners to a table of four women and serves them in a random manner. Find the probability that (a) each woman receives the dinner she ordered, (e) none of the women receives the dinner she ordered.

Example 3   Four birds are released from their individual cages. After flying around for an hour, they are put back into the cages in a random fashion, one bird per cage. Find the probability that (a) each bird is returned to its own cage, (e) no bird is returned to its own cage.

ANOTHER CARD MATCHING PROBLEM

Now suppose that, in the preceding card matching problem, the white cards are dealt one at a time *replacing* each card after it is dealt and then reshuffling the cards. Find the probability that the person obtains exactly (a) 4 matches, (b) 3 matches, (c) 2 matches, (d) 1 match, (e) no matches.

Solution   The sample space is still the set of all possible ways the 4 white cards can be dealt. However, in this case, any one of the 4 white cards can be dealt in any one of the 4 positions. Therefore, we have $4 \times 4 \times 4 \times 4 = 4^4 = 256$ ways of dealing out the 4 white cards in the prescribed manner. Therefore, the sample space consists of 256 elements. If we should so desire, we could designate each element of the sample space by a 4-term sequence (x, y, z, w) where x, y, z, and w are integers ≥ 1 and ≤ 4. Then we could list all 256 sequences and answer parts (a), (b), (c), (d), and (e) by counting sequences. Since this is a tedious process, we shall use another method to find the required probabilities, a method in which we count sequences without actually listing them.

Now, to obtain 4 matches, we must deal the white cards in the order 1, 2, 3, 4. Therefore, we have only 1 way of obtaining 4 matches and the probability is $1/256$. Note that this probability is substantially smaller than in the preceding problem. To obtain exactly 3 matches, we must deal matching cards in 3 positions and this can be done in only one way. However, the non-matching position may be any one of the 4 positions, and the non-matching card may be any one of 3 cards. Hence, there are $4 \times 3 = 12$ ways to deal the white cards and obtain exactly 3 matches. Therefore, the probability is 12/256. Note that in the earlier problem, this probability was zero because the cards were being dealt *without* replacement.

To obtain exactly 2 matches, we need 2 matching positions, which can occur in 6 ways. They are positions 1 and 2, 1 and 3, 1 and 4, 2 and 3, 2 and 4, 3 and 4. Now, the matching cards can be dealt in only 1 way in each case, but the non-matching cards can be dealt in 3 different ways into each of the 2 non-matching positions, yielding a total of 9 ways of dealing the non-matching cards. Therefore, we have $6 \times 9 = 54$ ways of dealing the cards and obtaining exactly 2 matches. Consequently, the probability is 54/256.

Now, we may obtain 1 match by dealing the 1 matching card in any one of 4 positions, and we may deal any one of 3 non-matching cards in any one of the 3 non-matching positions. Thus, we obtain $4 \times 3 \times 3 \times 3 = 108$ ways of obtaining 1 match, and a probability of 108/256.

Finally, we obtain no matches by dealing any one of the 3 non-matching cards into any one of the 4 positions for a total of $3^4 = 81$ ways. Therefore, the probability of obtaining no matches is 81/256.

This type of matching problem is sometimes designated as a *matching problem with replacement*. An example of a similar problem is the following one.

A man tosses a single die 6 consecutive times. A match occurs if the number that appears on the die is the same as the number of the toss. Find the probability that the man obtains exactly 6 matches, 5 matches, 4 matches, 3 matches, 2 matches, 1 match, and no matches.

THE STICK PROBLEM

Suppose there are 4 sticks: a red, a white, a blue, and a green one. Each stick is broken into a *long* and a *short* part. The 8 parts are mixed and then arranged side by side into 8 positions. Four new sticks are formed by combining the parts in positions 1 and 2, the parts in positions 3 and 4, the parts in positions 5 and 6, and the parts in positions 7 and 8. Find the probability that

(a) each new stick is an original stick

(b) each new stick is composed of a long and a short part, not necessarily of the same color

(c) each new stick is composed of either two long parts or two short parts.

The sample space is the set of all possible arrangements of the 8 parts into 8 positions. But there are 8 ways of filling the first position, 7 ways of filling the second position, 6 ways of filling the third position, and so on, down to 2 ways of filling the seventh position and 1 way of filling the eighth position. Therefore, the sample space has $8 \cdot 7 \cdot 6 \cdot 5 \cdot 4 \cdot 3 \cdot 2 \cdot 1$ outcomes. Let us count the total number of outcomes in which each new stick is an original stick. Any one of the 8 parts can appear in position 1. However, to obtain an original stick in positions 1 and 2, we must have in position 2 the one remaining part that has the same color as the part in position 1. Therefore, the part that appears in position 2 is determined by the one that appears in position 1. Hence, there are 8 ways of obtaining an original stick in the first two positions. Now, after the original stick is formed in the first two positions, any one of the remaining 6 parts can appear in position 3, and position 4 must therefore have the one remaining part that has the same color as the one in position 3. Consequently, there are 6 ways of obtaining an original stick in positions 3 and 4 following an original stick in positions 1 and 2. Continuing, we find that there are 4 ways of obtaining an original stick in positions 5 and 6, and 2 ways in positions 7 and 8. The total is $8 \cdot 1 \cdot 6 \cdot 1 \cdot 4 \cdot 1 \cdot 2 \cdot 1$, and thus the probability that every new stick is an original stick is $8 \cdot 1 \cdot 6 \cdot 1 \cdot 4 \cdot 1 \cdot 2 \cdot 1 \div 8 \cdot 7 \cdot 6 \cdot 5 \cdot 4 \cdot 3 \cdot 2 \cdot 1 = 1/(7 \cdot 5 \cdot 3 \cdot 1) = 1/105$.

Solution (b)

We must determine the number of arrangements in which each new stick is composed of a long and a short part, not necessarily of the same color. Once again, any one of the 8 parts may appear in position 1. Now, regardless of whether position 1 has a long or a short part, there will be 4 parts of the other type that can appear in position 2. For example, if position 1 has a long part, then there are 4 remaining short parts and, since color is being ignored in this case, any one of the 4 short parts can appear in position 2. After positions 1 and 2 are taken care of, any one of the remaining 6 parts can appear in position 3. But, once again, this part will be either long or short and so there will be 3 remaining parts of the opposite type to fill position 4. Continuing, we find that position 5 can be filled in any one of 4 ways, position 6 in any one of 2 ways, position 7 in any one of 2 ways, and position 8 in one way. Hence, the total number of outcomes in which each new stick is composed of a long and a short part is $8 \cdot 4 \cdot 6 \cdot 3 \cdot 4 \cdot 2 \cdot 2 \cdot 1$ and the probability is $8 \cdot 4 \cdot 6 \cdot 3 \cdot 4 \cdot 2 \cdot 2 \cdot 1 \div 8 \cdot 7 \cdot 6 \cdot 5 \cdot 4 \cdot 3 \cdot 2 \cdot 1 = 8/35$.

Finally, as an exercise, prove that the answer to (c) is $3/35$.

The stick problem has its roots in biology. It seems that whenever certain body cells are subjected to an overdose of radiation, some of the chromosomes split into fragments that sometimes reunite later on. The chromosomes play the role of the sticks, with their *long* part corresponding to the part that contains what biologists call the centromere. If the split chromosomes reunite in such a way that two *long* or two *short* parts combine, then the cell dies.

We shall now give some other examples that are similar to the stick problem.

Example 1 A man has a one dollar bill, a five dollar bill, a ten dollar bill, and a twenty dollar bill. He tears each bill in half, mixes the pieces, and forms new bills in the same way that the new sticks were formed in the stick problem. Find the probability that (a) each new bill is an original one, (b) each new bill consists of a left half and a right half, not necessarily from the same bill, (c) each new bill is composed of either two left halves or two right halves.

Example 2 A woman has four pairs of gloves in a drawer, each pair in a different color. She removes the gloves in a haphazard manner and forms new pairs in a way similar to the way in which the new sticks were formed in the stick problem. Find the probability that (a) each new pair is an original one, (b) each new pair consists of a glove for the left hand and a glove for the right hand, but not necessarily in the same color, (c) each new pair consists of either two gloves for the left hand or two gloves for the right hand.

Example 3 Four married couples are given a group of eight tickets for adjacent seats in an auditorium. One of the husbands hands out one ticket to each person in a random fashion, keeping the last ticket for himself. Find the probability that (a) each married couple sits in a pair of adjacent seats, (b) each pair of adjacent seats contains one man and one woman, but not necessarily a married couple, (c) each pair of adjacent seats contains either two men or two women.

PROBLEMS

20.1 Suppose a counter is at the origin on a coordinate line. Find the probability that the counter is
   (a) at the point 3 after 5 tosses of the coin
   (b) at the point 3 after 6 tosses
   (c) at the point -2 after 6 tosses.

20.2 Suppose a counter is at the point 2 on a coordinate line. Find the probability that the counter is
   (a) at the point 4 after 8 tosses of the coin (Appendix)

(b) at the point -4 after 8 tosses

(c) at the point 5 after 6 tosses

(d) at the point 3 after 5 tosses.

20.3 In the elevator problem given in the text, find the probability that
(a) nobody gets off on the first floor
(b) exactly 2 people get off on the second floor
(c) at least 2 people get off on the second floor
(d) at most 1 person gets off on the third floor.

20.4 Repeat parts (a) and (b) of the elevator problem given in the text with *4* people and a *4*-story building. Also repeat parts (a), (b), (c), and (d) of Problem 20.3 under these same conditions.

20.5 Repeat *each* of the two card matching problems given in the text using *3* cards, and find the probability that the person obtains
(a) exactly 1 match
(b) no matches
(c) at least 1 match.

20.6 Repeat each of the two card matching problems given in the text using *5* cards, and find the probability that the person obtains exactly
(a) 5 matches   **(b)** 4 matches   **(c)** 3 matches
(d) 2 matches   **(e)** 1 match   **(f)** no matches.

20.7 Repeat the stick problem given in the text with 5 distinctly colored sticks.

20.8 Repeat the stick problem given in the text with 6 distinctly colored sticks.

20.9 One thousand cars are in a parking lot and are assigned numbers from 1 through 1000. Five cars leave the lot one at a time. What is the probability that their corresponding numbers are in an ascending order, not necessarily consecutive?

20.10 A standard deck of 52 cards is dealt out in a row. Find the probability that the ace and king of spades are next to one another (Appendix).

20.11 A nightclub singer has a repertoire of 8 songs. Each night he does *one* show consisting of *2 distinct* songs chosen at random from his repertoire. Suppose you go to the nightclub on 3 consecutive nights. What is the probability that
(a) you do not hear the same song on 2 consecutive nights
(b) you hear the same opening song each night
(c)* you do not hear the same song on 3 consecutive nights? (Appendix)

20.12* A man has 4 pairs of shoes in a suitcase, each pair in a different color. He unpacks the shoes one at a time in a random fashion. Find the probability that after unpacking the first four shoes, he has
(a) 2 matching pairs (Appendix)
(b) 1 matching pair
(c) no matching pairs.

Section 21

SYSTEMATIC COUNTING

In this section we will derive some general formulas that will enable us to count with speed and accuracy. In the preceding two sections, most of the counting was done in an elementary direct way since the numbers involved were small. We would now like to develop the machinery that will assist us in doing problems of a more general nature later on.

At the end of Section 19, we saw that if we had 10 distinctly numbered cards, we could draw 3 of them, one at a time *without replacement*, in $10 \cdot 9 \cdot 8$ ways. Now, suppose we have n distinctly numbered cards where n is any positive integer. We will determine the number of ways in which we can select r cards, one at a time *without* replacement, where r is any positive integer less than or equal to n. Observe that there are n ways of selecting the first card, $n - 1$ ways of selecting the second card, $n - 2$ ways of selecting the third card, . . . , and $n - (r - 1)$ ways of selecting the r-th card. Hence, there are $n(n - 1)(n - 2) \cdots (n - (r - 1))$ ways of selecting r cards from a deck of n cards. If $r = n$, we obtain $n(n - 1)(n - 2) \ldots (3)(2)(1)$ ways of making the selections. The latter product is usually denoted by $n!$ and called "n factorial." The former product can then be expressed as the quotient $n!/(n - r)!$ and is usually denoted by $P(n, r)$. Note that when $r = n$, we obtain $P(n, n) = n!/0! = n!$ since $0!$ is conventionally defined to be 1.

For example, in the previously mentioned problem where 3 cards are drawn from a deck of 10 cards, we have $n = 10, r = 3, n - r = 7$, and we obtain $P(10, 3) = 10!/7! = 10 \cdot 9 \cdot 8$. If we draw all 10 cards in succession, there are 10! ways of making the selections where $10! = 3,628,800$. In fact, if we use a standard deck of 52 playing cards, there are 52! ways of drawing the 52 cards in succession. Before the student attempts to calculate 52!, we warn him that 52! is a 68-digit number and it would take almost one complete line in this textbook to write it.

In the preceding discussion, we used a model in which selections were made from a deck of cards. However, most of what we did can be applied to general *sampling* problems where we have n distinct objects and we select a specific number of them one at a time *without* replacement. Hence there are $n!$ ways of drawing all n objects and $n!/(n - r)!$ ways of selecting only r of the n objects.

For example, suppose a man has 5 different coins in his pocket. In how many ways can he draw 3 of them from his pocket? In how many ways can he draw all 5 coins? Applying the formula, we obtain $P(5, 3) = 5!/2! = 5 \cdot 4 \cdot 3 = 60$ ways as the answer to the first question, and $5! = 120$ ways as the answer to the second question.

We can also apply the preceding formulas to problems that involve *permutations* or *rearrangements* of objects that are arranged in a row. In this case, $n!$ is the number of *distinct permutations or rearrangements of the n objects* and $P(n, r) = n!/(n - r)!$ is the number of *permutations of n objects taken r at a time*. Note that this is just a special case of the general sampling problem, since we must choose 1 of the n objects to occupy the first position in the row, 1 of the remaining $n - 1$ objects to occupy the second position, and so on.

For example, suppose a student has 5 different books that he wishes to arrange on a shelf. Then there are 5! distinct arrangements of the 5 books. However, suppose there is only room on the shelf for 3 of the 5 books. Then there are $P(5, 3) = 5!/2! = 5 \cdot 4 \cdot 3 = 60$ ways of arranging the 5 books taking only 3 at a time.

In what follows, we again make use of a card sampling model. Suppose there is a deck of 10 distinctly numbered cards and we are dealt 4 of them. How many 4-card hands are there? Here we are *not* interested in the *order* in which the 4 cards are dealt, but only in the final result. For example, suppose that cards numbered 1, 8, 6, and 3 are dealt in that order. We would obtain the same hand even if the cards were dealt in the order 6, 8, 1, and 3, or in the order 3, 6, 8, and 1, and so on. Hence, the cards numbered 1, 3, 6, and 8 constitute only 1 hand *regardless* of the *order* in which they are dealt. Therefore, to determine the total number of hands, we observe that any group of 4 cards can be dealt in exactly 4! ways. If x is the number of distinct 4-card hands, then $(4!)x$ is the total number of ways in which they can be dealt. However, from the preceding discussion, we know that there are $10!/6!$ ways in which 4 of 10 cards can be dealt. Therefore, $(4!)x = 10!/6!$, which implies that $x = 10!/4!6! = 10 \cdot 9 \cdot 8 \cdot 7/4 \cdot 3 \cdot 2 \cdot 1 = 210$.

Generalizing the preceding result, we may ask how many r-card hands can be dealt from an n-card deck? Thus, we wish to determine the number of r-element subsets of the n-element set of cards. If we let $C(n, r)$ stand for this number, then we find that the total number of ways of dealing r cards is $r! \, C(n, r)$, since each distinct group of r cards can be dealt in $r!$ ways. However, from the earlier discussion, we know that there are $P(n, r) = n!/(n - r)!$ ways to deal r cards. Therefore, $r! C(n, r) = P(n, r) = n!/(n - r)!$ and so $C(n, r) = P(n, r)/r! = n!/r!(n - r)!$ This formula can also be applied in any problem where we choose r objects from a set of n objects without regard for the order in which they are selected. Such a collection of r objects is called a *combination* of the n objects taken r at a time. Hence, $C(n, r)$ represents the formula for the number of *combinations of* n *objects taken* r *at a time*.

As an example, suppose a woman is in a store that sells phonograph records. She finds 5 records that she likes, but she has only enough money to buy 3 of the 5 records. In how many ways can she purchase only 3 of the 5 records? We obtain the answer from the formula for $C(n, r)$ with $n = 5$ and $r = 3$, arriving at $5!/3!2! = 5 \cdot 4/1 \cdot 2 = 10$ ways that the purchase can be made.

In addition, this formula can be applied in the *counter problem* of Section 20, where we had to determine the number of distinct ways of distributing 2 L's into 6 positions in a sequence. Hence, we had to find the number of 2-element subsets of the set of 6 positions. The preceding formula yields $C(6, 2) = 6!/2!4! = 15$ as the correct answer. Also, in the *card matching* problems of Section 20, we had to determine the number of ways of obtaining exactly 2 matches in 4 tries. This involved counting the number of ways we could select 2 of the 4 positions to be matching positions. The preceding formula yields $C(4, 2) = 4!/2!2! = 6$ as the correct answer.

Finally, there is another type of problem that is related to *both* the permutation and the combination problems. Suppose a deck of colored cards (without numbers) consists of 4 red, 3 white, and 2 blue cards. In how many *distinguishable* ways can these cards be dealt out in a row? This problem is solved by looking at it from the following point of view. The 4 red cards can appear among the 9 positions in $C(9, 4)$ ways, the 3 white cards can appear among the remaining 5 positions in $C(5, 3)$ ways, and the 2 blue cards must appear in the remaining 2 positions in $C(2, 2) = 1$ way. Therefore, we have $C(9, 4) \times C(5, 3) \times$

$$C(2, 2) = \frac{9!}{4!5!} \frac{5!}{3!2!} \frac{2!}{2!0!} = \frac{9!}{4!3!2!} = 1260 \text{ } distinguishable \text{ ways of deal-}$$

ing the cards.

To generalize the preceding result, suppose we have a deck of n colored cards *without numbers* composed of r_1 cards of one color, r_2 cards of a second color, r_3 cards of a third color,..., and r_k cards of a k th color, where $r_1 + r_2 + r_3 + \ldots + r_k = n$. In how many distinguishable ways can they be dealt out in a row? We observe that the r_1 cards of the first color can appear among the n positions in $C(n, r_1)$ ways; the r_2 cards of the second color can appear in the remaining $n - r_1$ positions in $C(n - r_1, r_2)$ ways; the r_3 cards of the third color can appear in the remaining $n - r_1 - r_2$ positions in $C(n - r_1 - r_2, r_3)$ ways;...; the r_k cards of the kth color can appear in the remaining r_k positions in $C(r_k, r_k) = 1$ way. Therefore, the total number of distinguishable deals is

$$C(n, r_1) \times C(n - r_1, r_2) \times C(n - r_1 - r_2, r_3) \times \ldots \times C(r_k, r_k)$$

$$= \frac{n!}{r_1!(n - r_1)!} \frac{(n - r_1)!}{r_2!(n - r_1 - r_2)!} \frac{(n - r_1 - r_2)!}{r_3!(n - r_1 - r_2 - r_3)!} \cdots \frac{r_k!}{r_k!0!}$$

$$= \frac{n!}{r_1!r_2!r_3! \ldots r_k!}.$$

This formula can be applied to many types of problems that are *mixtures of combinations and permutations*.

As a final example, suppose a child has a dozen plastic blocks, all of the same size but in different colors. Suppose further that 5 blocks are red, 4 are white, 2 are blue, and 1 is green. In how many distinguishable ways can the child arrange the 12 blocks in a row? To answer this question, we use the preceding formula with $n = 12$, $r_1 = 5$, $r_2 = 4$, $r_3 = 2$, $r_4 = 1$, arriving at $\frac{12!}{5! \ 4! \ 2! \ 1!} = 83160$ ways in which the child can arrange the 12 blocks in a row.

PROBLEMS

21.1 (a) A deck of cards consists of 10 distinctly numbered cards. In how many ways can 4 cards be selected *with replacement* of each card after it is drawn? Find the probability that the 4 cards selected are distinctly numbered.

(b) A deck of cards consists of n distinctly numbered cards. In how many ways can r cards be selected *with replacement* where $1 \le r \le n$? Find the probability that the r cards selected are distinctly numbered.

21.2 A man selects 10 cards *with replacement* from a standard deck of 52 cards. Find the probability that
(a) exactly 4 cards are aces (Appendix)
(b) exactly 5 cards are picture cards
(c) *both* conditions (a) and (b) hold.

21.3 A man tosses a pair of dice, one of them red, the other green. Find the probability that
(a) exactly 3 of 8 tosses result in an outcome of 7 (Appendix)
(b) exactly 2 of 10 tosses result in an outcome of 11
(c) in 10 tosses, he obtains 4 sevens, 3 nines, 2 tens, and 1 twelve.

21.4 (a) How many distinct 6-digit automobile license plate numbers can be made from the digits 1, 2, 3, 4, 5, 6, 7, 8, and 9 if no digit appears more than once?
(b) Repeat part (a) with no restrictions on the number of times a digit appears.
(c) In part (b), find the probability that an *even* license plate number is formed.

21.5 Repeat Problem 20.9 letting
(a) 10 cars leave the lot one at a time
(b) n cars leave the lot one at a time.

21.6 (a) A standard deck of 52 cards is dealt out in a row. In how many ways can the ace, king, and queen of spades be adjacent to one another in any order (see Problem 20.10)?
(b) Repeat part (a) with the ace, king, queen, jack, and ten of spades.
(c) Repeat part (a) with *any* specific group of k cards where $1 < k < n$.
(d) Find the corresponding probabilities in each of the preceding parts.

21.7 (a) How many 5-card hands can be dealt from a standard deck of 52 cards?
(b) Find the probability that a 5-card hand has at least one card in each suit (Appendix).
(c) Find the probability that a 5-card hand has 3 spades and 2 hearts (Appendix).

21.8 (a) How many 13-card hands can be dealt from a standard deck of 52 cards?
(b) Find the probability that a 13-card hand has exactly 1 card in each of the 13 ranks.
(c) Find the probability that a 13-card hand has 4 spades, 5 hearts, 3 clubs, and 1 diamond.
(d) Find the probability that a 13-card hand has 3 aces, 2 kings, 3 jacks, 2 tens, 1 nine, and 2 sevens.

21.9 (a) In how many ways can a football, a baseball, a basketball, and a golf ball be arranged in a row on a shelf?
(b) In how many ways can they be placed in 6 numbered boxes with no more than one ball in a box?

21.10 (a) In how many distinguishable ways can 3 indistinguishable footballs, 4 indistinguishable baseballs, 5 indistinguishable basketballs, and 6 indistinguishable golf balls be arranged in a row on a shelf?

(b) In how many distinguishable ways can these 18 balls be placed in 25 numbered boxes with no more than one ball in a box?

21.11 A deck of 8 cards consists of 4 distinctly numbered red cards and 4 distinctly numbered black cards. In how many ways can they be arranged in a row if
  (a) all red cards are adjacent to one another *and* all black cards are adjacent to one another (Appendix)
  (b) only the red cards need be adjacent to one another
  (c) no two red cards are adjacent
  (d) there is a black card at each end of the row?

21.12 Repeat Problem 20.12 with
  (a) 6 pairs of shoes in the suitcase
  (b) n pairs of shoes in the suitcase, where n is any positive integer greater than 6.

21.13* A man has n pairs of shoes in a suitcase, each pair in a different color. He unpacks the shoes one at a time in a random fashion. Find the probability that after unpacking the first $2r$ shoes, where $2r < n$, he has
  (a) no matching pairs
  (b) exactly one matching pair
  (c) exactly two matching pairs.

21.14 Repeat parts (a), (b), and (c) of *the stick problem* of Section 20 with
  (a) 8 distinctly colored sticks
  (b)* n distinctly colored sticks where n is any positive *even* integer greater than 2 (Appendix)
  (c)* n distinctly colored sticks where n is any positive *odd* integer greater than 1.

21.15 Repeat Problem 20.11 with the following new conditions:
  (1) the singer has a repertoire of 12 songs
  (2) each show consists of 3 distinct songs.

Section 22

GENERAL FORMULAS IN PROBABILITY

In this section, we shall state, in their most general form, three problems that were discussed earlier in Section 20. They are the *counter* problem, the *elevator* problem, and the *card matching* problem *with* replacement. Using the counting methods explained in Section 21, we shall develop general formulas for the solution to these three problems. We shall also ask the student to apply the general formulas in some exercises and in the problems that follow this section.

THE COUNTER PROBLEM

Before proceeding, the student should review the material on this problem as it was presented in Section 20. In generalizing this problem, we assume that the counter is at the origin on a coordinate line and we wish to find the probability that it ends up at the point with coordinate x after n jumps, where n is any positive integer and x is an integer with $-n \leq x \leq n$. The sample space is the set of all sequences of n jumps, and each element of the sample space can be represented by a sequence of L's and R's. Since there are n positions in the sequence and only 2 ways of filling each position, the total number of sequences in the sample space is $\underbrace{2 \times 2 \times 2 \times \ldots \times 2}_{n \text{ factors}} = 2^n$. To find the probability that the counter ends up at the point with coordinate x, we must count the elements of the set of all sequences that correspond to the counter being at x after the n th jump. If r is the number of right jumps and f is the number of left jumps that occur in any sequence, then the sequences we are looking for must satisfy the relations $r - f = x$ and $r + f = n$. Adding the equations and solving for r, we obtain $r = \dfrac{n + x}{2}$. This is the number of right jumps required in a sequence that corresponds to the counter being at the point x after n jumps. Therefore, we must count the sequences that have $\dfrac{n + x}{2}$ right jumps among their n positions. But the $\dfrac{n + x}{2}$ right jumps can be distributed among the n positions of the sequence in precisely $C\left(n, \dfrac{n + x}{2}\right)$ ways. Therefore, the *probability that the counter ends up at the point* x *after* n *jumps is* $C\left(n, \dfrac{n + x}{2}\right)/2^n$.

Note that if either n or x is odd and the other one is even, then $\dfrac{n + x}{2}$ is *not* an integer and the probability that the counter ends up at the point x after n jumps is 0 (see Solution (b) to the counter problem in Section 20). Hence, n and x must *both* be odd or both be even in order to obtain a nonzero probability.

As an exercise, test this formula in part (a) of the counter problem in Section 20. Also apply this formula in Problems 20.1 and 20.2 and verify the answers that were obtained earlier.

THE ELEVATOR PROBLEM

Once again, before going on, the student should review the material on this problem that appears in Section 20. To generalize this problem, we assume that r people get on an elevator in the basement of a building that has n floors *above* the basement. To find the sample space, we must determine the total number of ways that the r people can get off the elevator on the n floors.

Suppose we indicate a distribution of the r people onto the n floors by the following symbolic representation using p's for the people and slant lines as floor dividers:

$$\text{pp/p/ppp//p/}\dots\text{/pp/p}$$

In this representation, we use r p's for the people and $n - 1$ slant lines to divide the people among the n floors. We interpret the preceding representation as the one that corresponds to the distribution given in the notation of Section 20 by the following sequence: $(2, 1, 3, 0, 1, \dots, 2, 1)$. For example, in the elevator problem of Section 20, we can use the following representations on the left to correspond to the sequences on the right:

ppppp//	(5, 0, 0)
pppp/p/	(4, 1, 0)
ppp//pp	(3, 0, 2)
p/ppp/p	(1, 3, 1)
pp/p/pp	(2, 1, 2).

Therefore, in this case, we may count the sequences in the sample space by counting the total number of distinguishable arrangements of the 5 p's and the 2 slant lines, since each sequence corresponds to such a representation in a unique way. However, this is just an application of the mixed permutation and combination formula mentioned at the end of Section 21 where we have 7 objects with the 5 p's alike and the 2 slant lines alike. The total number of arrangements is $7!/5!2! = 21$, and this agrees with the number of sample space elements in the elevator problem of Section 20.

Going back to the general case, we have r p's and $n - 1$ slant lines, and we look for the total number of arrangements of these $r + n - 1$ objects. By the formula of Section 21, we arrive at $(r + n - 1)!/r!(n - 1)!$, which can be stated more simply as $C(r + n - 1, r)$ (since, after all, we are counting the number of ways of placing r p's among the $r + n - 1$ spaces allotted for the p's *and* the slant lines).

In the *sample space* of the *general elevator problem*, we may ask questions like the following.

(a) Find the probability that at least one person gets off on each floor.

(b) Find the probability that the elevator is empty when it gets to the n-th floor.

(c) Find the probability that at least one person gets off on each floor except the first and second floors.

Solution (a)

We must count the total number of representations in which there is at least one p on each side of each slant line. Hence, we begin with the following representation using up exactly n p's, one on each side of each slant line (of course, in this case, we must assume that $r \geq n$ or else the probability is zero):

$$p/p/p/p/ \cdots /p/p$$

Now the remaining $r - n$ p's can be distributed among the n floors in any manner whatsoever. Hence, we may use the formula given earlier, with $r - n$ in place of r for the number of p's, arriving at $C(r - 1, r - n)$. Therefore, the probability that at least one person gets off on each floor is $C(r-1, r-n)/C(r+n-1, r)$. For example, if we apply this formula in Solution (a) in the elevator problem of Section 20, we obtain $C(4, 2)/C(7, 5) = 6/21$, which agrees with the answer arrived at in Section 20.

Solution (b)

If the elevator is empty when it gets to the nth floor, all r people got off on the first through the $(n-1)$-st floors. This corresponds to the distribution of the r p's among $n-1$ floors; hence, we need only the first $n-2$ slant lines as floor dividers. Therefore, we wish to find the total number of distinct arrangements of $r+(n-2)$ objects of which the r p's are alike and the $n-2$ slant lines are alike. Hence, we substitute $n-2$ for $n-1$ in our formula and obtain $C(r+n-2, r)$ as the total number of distinct arrangements. It follows that the probability is $C(r+n-2, r)/C(r+n-1, r)$. As an exercise, apply this formula in Solution (b) of the elevator problem in Section 20 and verify that the same answer is obtained.

Solution (c)

To find the probability that at least one person gets off on each floor except the first and second floors, we must count the number of distributions of the r people onto $n-2$ floors with at least one person getting off on each of the $n-2$ floors. We may use the formula $C(r-1, r-n)$ developed in part (a). However, in this case, we substitute $n-2$ for n, arriving at $C(r-1, r-(n-2))$. This is the total number of distributions of the r people onto the $n-2$ floors with at least one person per floor. Therefore, the probability is $C(r-1, r-(n-2))/C(r+n-1, r)$.

Note that if we wish to find the probability that nobody gets off on *only two* floors, where the floors are arbitrary, we would obtain $C(n, 2)C(r-1, r-(n-2))/C(r+n-1, r)$ as the answer, since there are $C(n, 2)$ ways of designating the two floors on which nobody gets off.

We previously asked questions (a), (b), and (c) in the sample space of the general elevator problem. As an exercise, answer these questions when $n = 10$ and $r = 15$.

Finally, the results of the general elevator problem may be applied in other problems in which r *indistinguishable* objects are placed in n *distinguishable* cells. Some examples of these related problems will be found among the problems at the end of the section.

THE CARD MATCHING PROBLEM

Before continuing, the student should review the material presented on the second card-matching problem in Section 20. To generalize it, we use a red deck and a white deck of cards, each deck numbered from 1 through n. We line up the red deck in numerical order and shuffle the white deck. We then deal cards from the white deck one at a time under the red deck, *replacing each card after it is dealt* and reshuffling the cards. We then determine the probability that the dealer obtains no matches, exactly 1 match, exactly 2 matches, exactly 3 matches, . . . , exactly $n - 1$ matches, and exactly n matches.

The sample space is the set of all possible ways in which the n white cards can be dealt. Since each deal can be represented by an n-termed sequence of the type $(x_1, x_2, x_3, \ldots, x_n)$ where each x_i is an integer with $1 \leq x_i \leq n$, the total number of elements in the sample space is

$$\overbrace{n \times n \times n \times \ldots \times n}^{n \text{ factors}} = n^n .$$

In order for a sequence to correspond to a deal in which no matches occur, none of the x_i's can equal i. Therefore, each x_i can be any one of the *other* $n - 1$ integers. Consequently, the number of sequences that represent deals in which no matches occur is

$$\overbrace{(n - 1) \times (n - 1) \times (n - 1) \times \ldots \times (n - 1)}^{n \text{ factors}} = (n - 1)^n .$$

Therefore, the probability of no matches is

$$(n - 1)^n/n^n = ((n - 1)/n)^n = (1 - 1/n)^n .$$

Apply this formula to part (e) of the second card matching problem in Section 20 and verify that the same answer is obtained.

It is also worth noting that the following result can be proved: for any integer $n > 4$, the number $(1 - 1/n)^n$ is *approximately* equal to $1/3$ (substitute $n = 5$ and $n = 10$ and work out the answer). Therefore, the probability is *independent* of the *number* of cards being used. This means that if 10, or 100, or 1000, or even 1,000,000 cards are used in each deck, the *probability* of obtaining *no matches* is always *approximately equal to* $1/3$.

To find the probability of obtaining *exactly* one match, we must count the sequences in which $x_i = i$ for precisely *one* value of i from 1 through n, while $x_i \neq i$ for any other values of i. There are n choices for the position in which $x_i = i$ and, after this position has been selected, any one of $n - 1$ numbers can appear in each of the $n - 1$ non-matching positions. This yields a total of $n(n - 1)^{n-1}$ sequences and so the probability of exactly one match is $n(n - 1)^{n-1}/n^n = (n - 1)^{n-1}/n^{n-1} = (1 - 1/n)^{n-1}$. Use this formula in part (d) of the second card matching problem in Section 20 and obtain the same answer.

Observe that $(1 - 1/n)^{n-1} = (1 - 1/n)^n (1 - 1/n)^{-1}$ and, for large enough n, $(1 - 1/n)^{-1}$ is approximately equal to 1. Hence, $(1 - 1/n)^{n-1}$

is approximately equal to $(1 - 1/n)^n$, and so the *probability* of *exactly one match* is also *approximately equal to* $1/3$ and is therefore *independent* of n when n is large enough.

To determine the probability of exactly two matches, we note that there are $C(n, 2)$ ways of choosing two positions i and j such that $x_i = i$ and $x_j = j$. Then each of the other $n - 2$ non-matching positions can be filled by any one of $n - 1$ numbers. This yields a total of $C(n, 2)(n - 1)^{n-2}$ sequences and thus the probability of exactly two matches is $C(n, 2)(n - 1)^{n-2}/n^n$. Use this formula in part (c) of the second card matching problem in Section 20 and obtain the same answer.

Observe also that, after some simplification, the preceding formula can be rewritten as $(1/2)(1 - 1/n)^n(1 - 1/n)^{-1}$. Hence, for large enough n, this probability is approximately equal to $(1/2)(1/3) = 1/6$ and is again *independent* of n.

Now, let us obtain a formula for the probability of exactly k matches where $2 < k \leq n$. In this case, there are $C(n, k)$ ways of choosing the matching positions where $x_i = i$ and, in the remaining $n - k$ non-matching positions, any one of $n - 1$ numbers can appear. Hence, the total number of sequences corresponding to exactly k matches is $C(n, k)(n - 1)^{n-k}$ and the probability is $C(n, k)(n - 1)^{n-k}/n^n$. Substitute $k = 3$ and $k = 4$ into this formula, and apply it in parts (a) and (b) of the second card matching problem in Section 20. Observe that the answers obtained are the same.

Finally, we notice that the preceding formula may be rewritten as

$$\frac{n(n - 1)(n - 2)\ldots(n - (k - 1))(n - 1)^{n-k}}{k!n^kn^{n-k}}$$

$$= \frac{1}{k!}\frac{n}{n}\frac{(n - 1)}{n}\frac{(n - 2)}{n}\ldots\frac{(n - (k - 1))}{n}\left(\frac{n - 1}{n}\right)^{n-k}$$

$$= \frac{1}{k!}1(1 - 1/n)(1 - 2/n)\ldots(1 - (k - 1)/n)(1 - 1/n)^n(1 - 1/n)^{-k}.$$

For large enough n, all the factors in the preceding product are *approximately* equal to 1 *except* for $1/k!$ and $(1 - 1/n)^n$. The latter factor, as mentioned earlier, is approximately equal to $1/3$. Therefore, when n is large enough, the formula for the *probability of exactly* k *matches is approximately equal to* $(1/3)(1/k!)$ and depends only on the number of matches k and *not* on the number of cards n. Note that for $k = 0$, $k = 1$, and $k = 2$, we obtain the same approximations as we did earlier, namely $1/3$, $1/3$, and $1/6$, respectively.

PROBLEMS

22.1 In the counter problem, find the probability that the counter is at
   (a) the point 4 after 12 tosses of the coin
   (b) the point 6 after 12 tosses of the coin
   (c) the point 16 after 20 tosses of the coin.

22.2* Suppose a deck of 4 cards consists of 1 red, 1 white, 1 blue, and 1 green card. A counter is at the origin in a coordinate *plane*. The cards are shuffled and one is selected and replaced. If the card drawn is red, the counter is moved 1 unit to the right; if the card is white, the counter is moved 1 unit to the left; if the card is blue, the counter is moved 1 unit up; if the card is green, the counter is moved 1 unit down. Find the probability that after 8 cards are selected, the counter is at
   (a) the point with coordinates (1, 1) (Appendix)
   (b) the point with coordinates (2, 4)
   (c) the point with coordinates (1, 3).
   (*Hint.* The sample space consists of all possible sequences having 8 positions that are filled with any of the 4 symbols R, L, U, and D.)

22.3 Fifteen distinguishable people get on an empty bus that has 40 numbered seats. In how many ways can they all be seated?

22.4 Let each of the 12 months of the year represent a cell. In how many ways can the birthdays of 30 people be distributed among the months of the year? Find the probability that none of the 30 people has a birthday in July. What is the probability that at least one person has a birthday in each of the 12 months? (See Example 4 following the *elevator* problem in Section 20.)

22.5 A standard deck of 52 cards is completely dealt out with 13 cards going to each of 4 players. In how many ways can the 13 spades be distributed (in this problem you may consider the 13 spades as *indistinguishable* from one another)? Find the probability that each player has at least one spade.

22.6 In how many ways can 25 typographical errors be distributed among the pages of a 20-page pamphlet (you may consider the typographical errors as *indistinguishable* from one another)? Find the probability that each page has at least one error. (See Example 5 following the *elevator* problem in Section 20.)

22.7 A set of dice contains 1 red, 1 white, and 1 blue die. What is the probability that on 2 consecutive tosses of the 3 dice the same configuration results?

22.8 A man tosses a set of 3 indistinguishable white dice *twice*. What is the probability that the same configuration results? Compare your answer with that of the preceding problem. (*Hint.* Let the digits 1, 2, 3, 4, 5, and 6 represent 6 cells, and let each of the dice represent an indistinguishable object. Then each toss of the dice is a distribution of 3 objects into 6 cells. (Also, see the discussion following Example 6 in the *elevator* problem of Section 20.)

22.9* A man tosses a set of 3 indistinguishable white dice. Find the probability that
   (a) all three numbers that show are the same

(b) two of the three numbers are the same

(c) all three numbers are distinct from one another.

(See the hint following the preceding problem.)

22.10 In the card matching problem with replacement as discussed in this section, let $n = 6$ and find the probability of obtaining exactly 0, 1, 2, 3, 4, 5, and 6 matches.

22.11 In the card matching problem with replacement as discussed in this section, let $n = 10$ and find the probability of obtaining

(a) no matches

(b) exactly one match

(c) at least one match

(d) exactly k matches for $1 < k \leq 10$.

22.12 In the card matching problem with replacement as discussed in this section, let $n = 52$ and find the probability of obtaining

(a) no matches

(b) at least one match

(c) at most one match

(d) more than two matches.

Bibliography

NUMBER THEORY

1. *Elements of Number Theory*, I. A. Barnett, Prindle, Weber and Schmidt, Boston, 1969
2. *Elementary Number Theory*, U. Dudley, Freeman, San Francisco, 1969
3. *Excursions in Number Theory*, C. S. Ogilvy and J. T. Anderson, Oxford University Press, N.Y., 1966
4. *Number Theory and Its History*, O. Ore, McGraw-Hill, N.Y., 1948
5. *Introduction to Number Theory*, J. Shockley, Holt, Rinehart and Winston, N.Y., 1967

HISTORY OF MATHEMATICS

6. *Men of Mathematics*, E. T. Bell, Simon and Schuster, N.Y., 1961
7. *Mathematics*, D. Bergamini, Life Science Library, Time Inc., N.Y., 1963
8. *A History of Mathematics*, C. Boyer, Wiley, N.Y., 1968
9. *Number, The Language of Science*, Fourth edition, T. Dantzig, Macmillan, N.Y., 1967
10. *Number Words and Number Symbols: A Cultural History of Numbers*, K. Menninger, M.I.T. Press, Cambridge, Mass., 1970
11. *The World of Mathematics* (4 Volumes), J. R. Newman, Simon and Schuster, N.Y., 1956
12. *Science Awakening*, B. L. Van Der Waerden, Oxford University Press, N.Y., 1961

PROBABILITY

13. *An Introduction to Probability Theory and Its Applications*, Volume 1, Third Edition, W. Feller, Wiley, N.Y., 1968
14. *Probability*, S. Goldberg, Prentice-Hall, Englewood Cliffs, N.J., 1960
15. *Fifty Challenging Problems in Probability*, F. Mosteller, Addison-Wesley, Reading, Mass., 1965
16. *Probability with Statistical Applications*, F. Mosteller, R. Rourke and G. Thomas, Addison-Wesley, Reading, Mass., 1961
17. *Mathematics of Choice*, I. Niven, Random House, N.Y., 1965

GENERAL MATHEMATICS

18. *The Significance of Mathematics*, H. Montague and M. Montgomery, Charles E. Merrill, Columbus, Ohio, 1963
19. *Mathematics, The Alphabet of Science*, M. Willerding and R. Hayward, Wiley, N.Y., 1968
20. *An Introduction to Mathematics*, B. K. Youse, Allyn and Bacon, Boston, 1970

BIBLIOGRAPHY

Appendix

1.4 (a) $a - b = a - c$ implies $a + (-b) = a + (-c)$ (by the definition of subtraction). Applying the cancellation law for addition, we obtain $-b = -c$. Multiplying both sides by -1, we arrive at $b = c$.

1.5 (a) Let $a \div b = x = a \div c$ where x is a nonzero integer. By the definition of division, it follows that $a = bx$, $a = cx$, and so $bx = cx$. Therefore $b = c$ by the cancellation law for multiplication.

2.1 (c) $a < b$ implies there exists a positive integer x such that $a + x = b$ (by the definition of $a < b$). Let c be a negative integer. Multiplying both sides of the preceding equation by c, we obtain $(a + x)c = bc$. This implies that $ac + xc = bc$ (by the distributive law). But, x positive and c negative imply that xc is a negative integer, and so $-(xc)$ is positive. Adding $-(xc)$ to both sides of the last equation, we arrive at $ac = bc + (-xc)$ where $-xc$ is a positive integer. This implies that $ac > bc$.

3.7 The product $n(n + 1)$ consists of 2 consecutive integers one of which must be even. Therefore, both of the given products, $n(n + 1)(n + 2)$ and $n(n + 1)(2n + 1)$, are divisible by 2. To prove both are divisible by 6 we need only show that each of the given products is divisible by 3. Whenever an integer n is divided by 3, the division algorithm states that the only possible remainders are 0, 1, and 2. Therefore, any integer n must have exactly one of the following forms:

$$n = 3k$$
$$n = 3k + 1$$
$$n = 3k + 2$$

where k is an integer. If n has the form $3k$, then n is divisible by 3 and so are both of the given products. If n has the form $3k + 2$, then $n + 1$ is of the form $3k + 3$ and is also divisible by 3. Therefore, both of the given products are divisible by 3 when n has the form $3k + 2$. Finally, if n has the form $3k + 1$, then $n + 2$ has the form $3k + 3$ and the first product is divisible by 3. In the second product, when n has the form $3k + 1$, the factor $2n + 1$ has the form $2(3k + 1) + 1 = 6k + 3$ and is divisible by 3. Consequently, the second product is also divisible by 3.

4.13 (a) Let $x = x_1 + b$ where $b = x_2 10 + x_3 10^2 + \ldots + x_n 10^{n-1}$. Since 2 divides every positive power of 10, it certainly divides b (by Theorems 3.1 and 3.2). Now if x_1 is divisible by 2, so is x (by Theorem 3.2).

On the other hand, if x is divisible by 2, then x_1 must also be divisible by 2 (by Theorem 3.4).

4.13 **(b)** Let $x = (x_1 + x_2 10) + b$ where

$$b = x_3 10^2 + x_4 10^3 + \ldots + x_n 10^{n-1}.$$

Since 4 divides every power of 10 from 10^2 on, 4 divides b (by Theorems 3.1 and 3.2). Now if $(x_1 + x_2 10)$ is divisible by 4, so is x (by Theorem 3.2); and if x is divisible by 4, then $x_1 + x_2 10$ must also be divisible by 4 (by Theorem 3.4).

4.16 **(a)** Let $x = x_1 + x_2 10 + x_3 10^2 + \ldots + x_n 10^{n-1}$. We now write $10 = 9 + 1$, $10^2 = 99 + 1$, $10^3 = 999 + 1, \ldots, 10^{n-1} = \overset{n-1 \text{ nines}}{\overline{999 \ldots 9}} + 1$. Therefore $x = x_1 + x_2(9 + 1) + x_3(99 + 1) + x_4(999 + 1) + \ldots + x_n(999 \ldots 9 + 1) = x_1 + x_2 9 + x_2 + x_3 99 + x_3 + x_4 999 + x_4 + \ldots + x_n 999 \ldots 9 + x_n = (x_1 + x_2 + x_3 + \ldots + x_n) + (x_2 + x_3 11 + x_4 111 + \ldots + x_n 111 \ldots 1)9$. It follows that $x = (x_1 + x_2 + x_3 + \ldots + x_n) + a \cdot 9$ where $a = x_2 + x_3 11 + x_4 111 + \ldots + x_n 111 \ldots 1$. If $x_1 + x_2 + x_3 + \ldots + x_n$ is divisible by 9, so is x (by Theorem 3.2) and if x is divisible by 9, then $x_1 + x_2 + x_3 + \ldots + x_n$ must also be divisible by 9 (by Theorem 3.4).

5.5 **(a)** If $d = (a + b, a - b)$, then d divides $a + b$ and $a - b$. It follows that d divides the *sum* $(a + b) + (a - b) = 2a$ and d divides the *difference* $(a + b) - (a - b) = 2b$ (by Theorem 3.2), and so $d \leq (2a, 2b)$. But $(a, b) = 1$ implies that $(2a, 2b) = 2$. Therefore $d \leq 2$, and $d = 1$ or $d = 2$ are the *only* possibilities.

8.8 **(b)** Suppose there are finitely many primes of the type $3k + 2$. Let P_1, $P_2, P_3, \ldots, P_r$ be a complete list of these primes. Construct the integer $N = 3(P_1 \cdot P_2 \cdots P_r) + 2$. Now N is of the type $3k + 2$ and N is certainly larger than P_r. Consequently N must be composite and has a factorization into a product of primes. But no prime of the type $3k + 2$ from the preceding list can divide N, because each P_i leaves a remainder of 2 when N is divided by it. It follows that N is a product of only primes having the form $3k + 1$. But any product of integers of the form $3k + 1$ must also be of the form $3k + 1$ since $(3k + 1)(3j + 1) = 9kj + 3k + 3j + 1 = 3(3kj + k + j) + 1$. This implies N must be of the type $3k + 1$; but N is not of this type since N has the form $3k + 2$ *by construction*. Therefore all the prime factors of N cannot be of the type $3k + 1$ and so there exists a prime factor P of N having the form $3k + 2$ that was *not* on the original list. It follows that the original list was not complete. This argument may be applied to any finite list of primes of the type $3k + 2$. Therefore no finite list of such primes is complete and so the number of such primes must be infinite.

9.3 **(a)/(b)** The number of divisors of an integer equals the product of the increased exponents in the standard prime factorization of the integer. To obtain a product of 7, the standard prime factorization must be of the form p^6 (since 7 is a prime). Since 2 is the smallest prime, the answer to part (a) is $2^6 = 64$. In part (b), the product of the increased exponents is 6. This can be obtained from any one of the following types of standard prime factorizations: p^5, $p \cdot q^2$, and $p^2 \cdot q$. The smallest integers of each type are $2^5 = 32$, $2 \cdot 3^2 = 18$, and $2^2 \cdot 3 = 12$. Therefore 12 is the answer to part (b).

9.8 From Problem **9.6(d)**, we know that $(ab)^* = (a)^*(b)^*$ for any pair of relatively prime integers a and b. Now suppose a and b are not relatively prime. Then a and b have at least one *common* prime factor p, and we may assume for the sake of simplicity, that the standard prime factorizations are of the form $a = p^i q^i r^k$ and $b = p^h s^f t^g$ where p, q, r, s, and t are all distinct primes. It follows that $(a)^* = (i + 1)(j + 1)(k + 1)$, $(b)^* = (h + 1)(f + 1)(g + 1)$, and $(a)^*(b)^* = (i + 1)(h + 1)(j + 1)(k + 1)(f + 1)(g + 1)$. On the other hand, $ab = p^{i+h} q^i r^k s^f t^g$ and $(ab)^* = (i + h + 1)(j + 1)(k + 1)(f + 1)(g + 1)$. Comparing the products $(a)^*(b)^*$ and $(ab)^*$, we see that the only *unequal* factors are $(i + 1)(h + 1)$ in $(a)^*(b)^*$ and $(i + h + 1)$ in $(ab)^*$. Since $(i + h + 1) < (i + 1)(h + 1)$, we conclude that $(ab)^* < (a)^*(b)^*$.

10.5 Theorem 6.1 states that for any two positive integers a and b, $[a,b] = \dfrac{ab}{(a, b)}$. From Problem **10.4**, we know that when $(a, b) = 1$, the preceding formula is valid. Now suppose that a and b are *not* relatively prime. Then a and b have at least one *common* prime factor p. For simplicity's sake, we may assume that the standard prime factorizations are of the form $a = p^i q^i r^k$ and $b = p^h s^f t^g$, where p, q, r, s, and t are all distinct primes and $i \leq h$. Then $(a, b) = p^i$ and $\dfrac{ab}{(a, b)} = p^h q^i r^k s^f t^g = [a, b]$.

11.9 **(b)** For the sake of brevity, let us look at only *one* prime power in the standard prime factorization of an integer n. Suppose p^i appears in the factorization of n and suppose further that i is a prime. Then the mosaic of n also has the factor p^i and the residual of the mosaic of n contains the factor $p \cdot i$. But $p \cdot i \leq p^i$ for all primes p and i, therefore the factor p^i of n contributes a factor to the residual that is less than or equal to p^i. Even when i is not a prime, the same thing occurs. (The student should check a few cases, say when $i = qr$ or $i = q^r$ where q and r are primes.) Consequently, *every* prime power appearing in the standard factorization of n also contributes a factor to the residual that is less than or equal to itself. Hence the residual of the mosaic of n will always be less than or equal to n.

11.9 **(c)** If n is not divisible by a perfect square, the standard prime factorization of n has only primes that appear with exponent 1. Therefore we may assume, for the sake of brevity, that $n = p \cdot q \cdot r$ where p, q, and r are distinct primes. But then the mosaic of n is $p \cdot q \cdot r$ and the residual of the mosaic of n is also equal to $p \cdot q \cdot r = n$. Therefore the statement is proven. The converse, however, is false. As an example, consider $n = 2^2 \cdot 3 = 12$. The mosaic of 12 is $2^2 \cdot 3$ and the residual of the mosaic is $2 \cdot 2 \cdot 3 = 12$. In fact, for any integer $n = 4m$ where m is odd and not divisible by a perfect square, the residual of the mosaic of n equals n.

11.13 **(d)** If $(a, b) = 1$, then a and b have no common primes appearing in their standard factorizations. Hence we may assume that the standard factorizations are $a = p^i q^j$ and $b = r^k s^h$ where p, q, r, and s are distinct primes. It follows that $(a)' = p \cdot (i)' \cdot q \cdot (j)'$, $(b)' = r \cdot (k)' \cdot s \cdot (h)'$, and $(a)'(b)' = p \cdot (i)' \cdot q \cdot (j)' \cdot r \cdot (k)' \cdot s \cdot (h)'$. But $ab = p^i q^j r^k s^h$ and so $(ab)' = p \cdot (i)' \cdot q \cdot (j)' \cdot r \cdot (k)' \cdot s \cdot (h)' = (a)'(b)'$.

11.13 **(e)** The converse is false. As an example, consider $a = 2$ and $b = 6$. Then $(2)' = 2$, $(6)' = 6$, and $(2)'(6)' = 12$. On the other hand, $(2 \cdot 6)' = (12)' = 12$, and so $(ab)' = (a)'(b)'$ with $(a, b) \neq 1$.

12.13 **(e)** The sum of the positive divisors of $p^i q^j$ is

$$(1 + q + q^2 + \ldots + q^j) + p(1 + q + q^2 + \ldots + q^j)$$
$$+ p^2(1 + q + q^2 + \ldots + q^j) + \ldots + p^i(1 + q + q^2 + \ldots + q^j)$$
$$= (1 + p + p^2 + \ldots + p^i)(1 + q + q^2 + \ldots + q^j)$$
$$= \frac{p^{i+1} - 1}{p - 1} \cdot \frac{q^{j+1} - 1}{q - 1}.$$

12.13 **(f)** Denote the answer to Problem **12.13(e)** by S. Then the sum of the positive divisors of $p^i q^j r^k$ is

$$S + S \cdot r + S \cdot r^2 + \ldots + S \cdot r^k = S(1 + r + r^2 + \ldots + r^k)$$
$$= S \frac{(r^{k+1} - 1)}{r} = \frac{p^{i+1} - 1}{p - 1} \cdot \frac{q^{j+1} - 1}{q - 1} \cdot \frac{r^{k+1} - 1}{r - 1}.$$

13.10 First we make a table of squares in the modulo-five system:

$$0^2 = 0$$
$$1^2 = 1$$
$$2^2 = 4$$
$$3^2 = 4$$
$$4^2 = 1.$$

From the table of squares, we see that $\sqrt{0} = 0$, $\sqrt{1} = 1$ and 4, and $\sqrt{4} = 2$ and 3—while $\sqrt{2}$ and $\sqrt{3}$ do not exist.

13.11 First we make a table of cubes in the modulo-five system:

$$0^3 = 0$$
$$1^3 = 1$$
$$2^3 = 3$$
$$3^3 = 2$$
$$4^3 = 4.$$

From the table of cubes, we see that $\sqrt[3]{0} = 0$, $\sqrt[3]{1} = 1$, $\sqrt[3]{2} = 3$, $\sqrt[3]{3} = 2$, and $\sqrt[3]{4} = 4$.

14.8 Let $n = 4m$ where m is any positive integer. Let $x = 2m$, $y = 1$, and $z = 1$. Then, for each integer $k > 2$, $x^k + y^k = (2m)^k + 1^k = 0 + 1^k = 1^k$.

15.7 **(a)** Suppose $ab = 0$ in R_p and $a \neq 0$. By the corollary to Theorem 15.1, $1/a$ exists in R_p. Multiplying both sides of the equation $ab = 0$ by $1/a$, we obtain $b = 0$.

15.7 **(b)** If m is not a prime, then there exist integers a and b such that $m = ab$, where $1 < a < m$ and $1 < b < m$. But then a and b are in R_m and $ab = 0$ in R_m. In R_9, $3 \cdot 3 = 0$ and in R_{12}, $2 \cdot 6 = 0$.

15.13 **(a)** Since $(n - 1)(n - 1) = 1$ in R_n, $1/(n - 1) = n - 1$ in R_n. Therefore the multiplicative inverse of $n - 1$ exists in R_n and so $n - 1$ divides every element in R_n (by the definition of division in R_n). Hence $n - 1$ must be equal to the greatest common divisor of any two elements a and b in R_n.

15.13 **(b)** If a and b are any two nonzero elements in R_p, then each one has a multiplicative inverse in R_p (by the corollary to Theorem 15.1).

Therefore a and b divide every element of R_p including 1, and so 1 is the least common multiple of a and b in R_p.

15.13 (c) Theorem 6.1 states that $[a, b] = \dfrac{ab}{(a, b)}$ for any positive integers a, b, and c. From parts (a) and (b) of Problem **15.13**, $[a, b] = 1$ and $(a, b) = n - 1$ for any pair of nonzero elements a and b in R_p. Therefore, if Theorem 6.1 is valid in R_p, we must have $\dfrac{ab}{n - 1} = 1$ for each pair of nonzero elements a and b in R_p. This implies that $ab = n - 1$ for any pair of nonzero elements a and b in R_p. But this is certainly *not* true for arbitrary choices of a and b. As examples, consider $a = 2$, $b = 3$ in R_5, and $a = 3$, $b = 5$ in R_7.

15.15 (d) By the corollary to Theorem 15.1, every nonzero element in R_p has a multiplicative inverse. But the multiplicative inverse of 1 is 1 and the multiplicative inverse of $p - 1$ is $p - 1$. Every other nonzero element in R_p has a multiplicative inverse that is *distinct* from itself. This follows from the fact that 1 and $p - 1$ are the *only* roots of the quadratic equation $x^2 - 1 = 0$ over R_p (see the corollary to Theorem 16.2). Therefore, taking the product of all the nonzero elements in R_p, results in the cancellation of all the elements that have distinct multiplicative inverses leaving us with the product $1 \cdot (p - 1) = p - 1$.

16.15 (a) Since $x^3 + 2x^2 + 2x + 1 = 0$ is a cubic equation, the only sure way to find all the roots is to substitute each element of R_7 and R_8 into the equation. Sometimes there is an easier way, provided one root can be obtained by *observation*. Then the cubic equation can be written as the product of a linear and a quadratic factor. The quadratic can then be solved by the methods exhibited in Section 16. For example, we can see that -1 is a root of $x^3 + 2x^2 + 2x + 1 = 0$ and so it can be factored into $(x + 1)(x^2 + x + 1) = 0$. In R_7, $-1 = 6$ is a root, and using the quadratic formula on $x^2 + x + 1 = 0$, we obtain $x = 2$ and $x = 4$ as the remaining roots. On the other hand, in R_8, $-1 = 7$ is a root but the quadratic formula cannot be used on $x^2 + x + 1 = 0$ in R_8. Substituting each of the elements of R_8 into the last equation, we find that none of them satisfies it. Consequently, 7 is the only root of $x^3 + 2x^2 + 2x + 1 = 0$ in R_8.

16.16 (c) Since $1/6$ does not exist in R_9, we cannot use the quadratic formula to help us factor $6x^2 + 5x + 4$. However by substituting each of the elements of R_9 into the equation $6x^2 + 5x + 4 = 0$, we find that $x = 7$ is the only root in R_9. Therefore, $x - 7$ is a factor and we finally obtain $6x^2 + 5x + 4 = (x - 7)(6x + 2)$ in R_9.

16.17 (a) We cannot use the quadratic formula in R_{10}, so we substitute each of the elements of R_{10} into the equation $x^2 + 7x + 2 = 0$. We obtain the roots $x = 1$, $x = 2$, $x = 6$, and $x = 7$, and so the corresponding factors are $x - 1$, $x - 2$, $x - 6$, and $x - 7$. To determine how to pair off the factors, we divide $x - 1$ into $x^2 + 7x + 2$ obtaining $x - 2$, and we divide $x - 6$ into $x^2 + 7x + 2$ obtaining $x - 7$. Therefore the two distinct factorizations of $x^2 + 7x + 2$ in R_{10} are $(x - 1)(x - 2)$ and $(x - 6)(x - 7)$. Note that if we pair off the factors in some other way, such as $(x - 1)(x - 6)$ or $(x - 2)(x - 7)$, we do *not* obtain a factorization of $x^2 + 7x + 2$.

17.15 (a) If $A + B = A$, then $\begin{pmatrix} a + x & b + y \\ c + z & d + w \end{pmatrix} = \begin{pmatrix} a & b \\ c & d \end{pmatrix}$. But two matrices are equal if and only if their corresponding entries are equal. Therefore, $a + x = a$ and x must be zero; $b + y = b$ and y must be zero; $c + z = c$ and z must be zero; $d + w = d$ and w must be zero. It follows that the matrix $B = \begin{pmatrix} x & y \\ z & w \end{pmatrix} = \begin{pmatrix} 0 & 0 \\ 0 & 0 \end{pmatrix}$.

17.15 (b) If $A + C = \begin{pmatrix} 0 & 0 \\ 0 & 0 \end{pmatrix}$, then $\begin{pmatrix} a + r & b + s \\ c + t & d + u \end{pmatrix} = \begin{pmatrix} 0 & 0 \\ 0 & 0 \end{pmatrix}$. Therefore, $a + r = 0$ and $r = -a$; $b + s = 0$ and $s = -b$; $c + t = 0$ and $t = -c$; $d + u = 0$ and $u = -d$. It follows that the matrix $C = \begin{pmatrix} r & s \\ t & u \end{pmatrix} = \begin{pmatrix} -a & -b \\ -c & -d \end{pmatrix}$.

18.4 (a) If $AI = A$, then $\begin{pmatrix} ar + bt & as + bu \\ cr + dt & cs + du \end{pmatrix} = \begin{pmatrix} a & b \\ c & d \end{pmatrix}$. This leads to two pairs of linear equations which may be solved simultaneously, the first pair for r and t and the second pair for s and u:

$$ar + bt = a \text{ and } cr + dt = c$$
$$as + bu = b \text{ and } cs + du = d$$

The solutions to the first pair of equations are $r = 1$ and $t = 0$ while the solutions to the second pair are $s = 0$ and $u = 1$. Therefore, $I = \begin{pmatrix} r & s \\ t & u \end{pmatrix} = \begin{pmatrix} 1 & 0 \\ 0 & 1 \end{pmatrix}$.

18.4 (b) If $AB = \begin{pmatrix} 1 & 0 \\ 0 & 1 \end{pmatrix}$, then $\begin{pmatrix} ax + by & az + bw \\ cx + dy & cz + dw \end{pmatrix} = \begin{pmatrix} 1 & 0 \\ 0 & 1 \end{pmatrix}$. This leads to two pairs of linear equations which may be solved simultaneously, the first pair for x and y and the second pair for z and w. Now follow the same argument as the one presented in the text at the beginning of Section 18.

19.4 (d) The sample space consists of $52 \cdot 51 = 2652$ outcomes. The total number of ways of selecting two cards, each from a different suit, is $52 \cdot 39 = 2028$. This follows from the fact that any one of the 52 cards may be chosen on the first draw, while on the second draw, we are restricted to one of the 39 cards that does not belong to the same suit as the card selected on the first draw. Consequently, the probability is $2028/2652$.

20.2 (a) If a counter begins at the point 2 on a coordinate line and ends up at the point 4, then the net difference between the number of right jumps and left jumps must be 2. Therefore, $r - f = 2$. But the number of jumps is 8, so $r + f = 8$. Adding the last two equations, we obtain $2r = 10$ which implies that $r = 5$ and $f = 3$. Now the student should verify that the number of jump sequences consisting of 5 right jumps and 3 left jumps is 56. It follows that the probability that the counter is at the point 4 after 8 tosses of the coin is $56/2^8$.

20.10 There are $52 \cdot 51 \cdot 50 \cdot \ \cdots \ \cdot 3 \cdot 2 \cdot 1$ ways of dealing 52 cards in a row, so the sample space consists of $52 \cdot 51 \cdot 50 \cdot \ \cdots \ \cdot 3 \cdot 2 \cdot 1$ outcomes. Now consider the ace and king of spades as being in a fixed block of 2 cards that is dealt as a single unit with two possible orders within the block (ace-king or king-ace). Then there are 50 other cards being dealt along with the fixed block, making a total of 51 objects being dealt. Therefore, we have 51 positions into which the block can be dealt, and $50 \cdot 49 \cdot 48 \cdot \cdots \cdot 3 \cdot 2 \cdot 1$ ways of dealing the other 50 cards. This results in a total of $2 \cdot 51 \cdot 50 \cdot 49 \cdot 48 \cdot \cdots \cdot 3 \cdot 2 \cdot 1$ ways of dealing the cards with the ace and king of spades being next to each other. It follows that the probability is $\dfrac{2 \cdot 51 \cdot 50 \cdot 49 \cdot 48 \cdot \cdots \cdot 3 \cdot 2 \cdot 1}{52 \cdot 51 \cdot 50 \cdot 49 \cdot 48 \cdot \cdots \cdot 3 \cdot 2 \cdot 1} = 2/52 = 1/26.$

20.11 (c) There are 8 ways of choosing the first song and 7 ways of choosing the second song on each night. This results in 56 ways of selecting the songs on each night and a sample space consisting of $(56)^3$ ways of selecting the songs for 3 consecutive nights. In order to find the number of ways in which the same song is *not* heard on 3 consecutive nights, we first find the number of ways that the same song *can be heard* on 3 consecutive nights, and subtract this number from $(56)^3$. Now there are 8 ways of selecting *one* song to be heard on 3 consecutive nights and 2 ways of positioning the song in each show on each night (first or second). Then there are 7 ways of choosing the other song to be sung each night. This leads to a total of $8 \cdot 2^3 \cdot 7^3$ ways in which one song can be sung on 3 consecutive nights. However, in the preceding computation, any sequence of shows in which the *same* two songs are sung each night is counted *twice*, once because one of the songs is repeated on consecutive nights and again because the other song is also repeated on consecutive nights. Therefore, to obtain a correct count of the number of ways the same song can be heard on 3 consecutive nights, we must find the number of ways that the same *two* songs can be sung each night and *subtract* this number from $8 \cdot 2^3 \cdot 7^3$. Now there are 28 ways of selecting, from the 8 songs in the repertoire, the two songs that are to be sung on all 3 nights. But, on each night, there are two orders in which the 2 songs can be sung. It follows that there are $28 \cdot 2^3$ ways in which the same 2 songs can be sung on 3 consecutive nights. Consequently, there are $8 \cdot 2^3 \cdot 7^3 - 28 \cdot 2^3$ ways that a song can be sung on 3 consecutive nights and $(56)^3 - 8 \cdot 2^3 \cdot 7^3 + 28 \cdot 2^3$ ways that the same song is *not* sung on 3 consecutive nights. The probability is given by
$$\frac{(56)^3 - 8 \cdot 2^3 \cdot 7^3 + 28 \cdot 2^3}{(56)^3}.$$

20.12 (a) There are 8 shoes in the suitcase, two in each of the four colors. In unpacking the shoes one at a time, there are $8 \cdot 7 \cdot 6 \cdot 5$ ways of selecting the first four shoes. Therefore the sample space has $8 \cdot 7 \cdot 6 \cdot 5$ outcomes. *Two* matching pairs can result by two different sequences of selections. We count the number of ways corresponding to each sequence and then we add them to obtain the total number of ways that two matching pairs can be chosen. The *first* sequence is the one in which the first and second shoes are of the same color. Then there are 8 ways of selecting the first shoe and 1 way of selecting the second shoe. But there are 6 ways of selecting the third shoe and 1 way of matching it on the fourth selection. Therefore, there are $8 \cdot 1 \cdot 6 \cdot 1$ ways corresponding to the first sequence in which 2 matching pairs are drawn. The *second* sequence is the one in which the first and second shoes are *not* of the same color. Then there are

8 ways of selecting the first shoe and 6 ways of selecting the second shoe. But the third shoe must match either the first or second shoe, and so there are 2 ways of choosing the third shoe. Finally, the fourth shoe can be selected in only 1 way since it must match the shoe that the third shoe did not match. Therefore, we have $8 \cdot 6 \cdot 2 \cdot 1$ ways corresponding to the second sequence in which two matching pairs are drawn. It follows that the total number of ways of choosing two matching pairs in the first four selections is $8 \cdot 1 \cdot 6 \cdot 1 + 8 \cdot 6 \cdot 2 \cdot 1$ and the corresponding probability is $\dfrac{8 \cdot 6 + 8 \cdot 6 \cdot 2}{8 \cdot 7 \cdot 6 \cdot 5} = \dfrac{1 + 2}{7 \cdot 5} = 3/35$.

21.2 **(a)** Any one of the 52 cards can be drawn on any one of the 10 selections yielding a sample space of $(52)^{10}$ outcomes. There are $C(10, 4)$ ways in which exactly 4 aces can be distributed among the 10 selections. Now, in each distribution, any one of 4 aces can appear on each of the selections in which aces are drawn. Hence the aces can appear in 4^4 different ways in each distribution. On the other hand, in each distribution, there are 48 non-aces that can appear on each of the remaining 6 selections in $(48)^6$ ways. It follows that there is a total of $C(10, 4)(4^4)(48)^6$ ways of choosing exactly 4 aces in 10 selections from a deck of 52 cards and the corresponding probability is $\dfrac{C(10, 4)(4^4)(48)^6}{(52)^{10}}$.

21.3 **(a)** On one toss of the dice, there are 36 possible outcomes of which 6 are sevens. On eight tosses in a row there are $(36)^8$ possible outcomes and this is the number of elements in the sample space. There are $C(8, 3)$ ways in which exactly 3 sevens can be distributed among the 8 tosses. Now in each distribution, a seven can occur in 6 different ways and so 3 sevens can occur in 6^3 different ways. On the other hand, in each distribution, a non-seven can occur in 30 ways and so 5 non-sevens can occur in $(30)^5$ ways. Therefore the total number of ways in which exactly 3 of 8 tosses result in a seven is $C(8, 3)(6^3)(30)^5$ and the corresponding probability is $\dfrac{C(8, 3)(6^3)(30)^5}{(36)^8}$.

21.7 **(b)** There are $C(52, 5)$ 5-card hands that can be dealt from a deck of 52 cards and so the sample space consists of $C(52, 5)$ outcomes. Now a 5-card hand that has at least one card in each of the 4 suits must consist of 2 cards of one suit and 1 card from each of the other 3 suits. But there are 4 ways of selecting the suit to which 2 of the 5 cards belong and $C(13, 2)$ ways of choosing the 2 cards from this suit. Each one of the other 3 cards is selected from a 13-card suit and can therefore be selected in 13 different ways. It follows that there are $4C(13, 2) \cdot 13^3$ 5-card hands that have at least one card in each suit and the corresponding probability is $\dfrac{4C(13, 2) \cdot 13^3}{C(52, 5)}$.

21.7 **(c)** There are $C(52, 5)$ possible 5-card hands. The 3 spades can come from a 13-card suit in $C(13, 3)$ ways, while the 2 hearts can come from a 13-card suit in $C(13, 2)$ ways. Therefore the total number of 5-card hands having 3 spades and 2 hearts is $C(13, 3) \cdot C(13, 2)$ and the corresponding probability is $\dfrac{C(13, 3) \cdot C(13, 2)}{C(52, 5)}$.

21.11 (a) All red cards are adjacent to one another and all black cards are adjacent to one another in any one of the two color sequences *rrrrbbbb* or *bbbbrrrr*. Within each sequence there are 4*!* ways of arranging the red cards and 4*!* ways of arranging the black cards. This leads us to $(4!)^2$ arrangements within each sequence and a total of $2(4!)^2$ arrangements in all.

21.14 **(B)** If each of the *n* sticks is broken into a long and a short part, then there are $2n$ parts to be mixed and arranged side by side into $2n$ positions. This can be done in $(2n)!$ ways since any one of the $2n$ parts can occupy the first position, any one of the remaining $2n - 1$ parts can occupy the second position, any one of the remaining $2n - 2$ parts can occupy the third position, and so on. Hence the sample space consists of $(2n)!$ outcomes. We now determine the number of ways in which each new stick formed is an *original* stick. Observe that any one of the $2n$ parts can appear in position 1, while only the one part that has the *same* color as the part in position 1 can appear in position 2. Then there are $2n - 2$ parts that can appear in position 3, and again, only 1 part that can appear in position 4, and so on. It follows that there are

$$(2n) \cdot 1 \cdot (2n - 2) \cdot 1 \cdot (2n - 4) \cdot 1 \cdot \cdots \cdot 4 \cdot 1 \cdot 2 \cdot 1$$

ways of arranging the sticks in such a way that each new stick formed is an original stick. Therefore the probability is

$$\frac{(2n) \cdot 1 \cdot (2n - 2) \cdot 1 \cdot (2n - 4) \cdot 1 \cdot \cdots \cdot 4 \cdot 1 \cdot 2 \cdot 1}{(2n)(2n - 1)(2n - 2)(2n - 3)(2n - 4)(2n - 5) \cdot \cdots \cdot 4 \cdot 3 \cdot 2 \cdot 1}$$

$$= \frac{1}{1 \cdot 3 \cdot 5 \cdot 7 \cdot \cdots \cdot (2n - 5)(2n - 3)(2n - 1)}.$$

We must now determine the probability that each new stick is composed of one *long* and one *short* part, not necessarily of the same color. In this case, any one of the $2n$ parts can occupy the first position while any one of the remaining *n* parts of the *opposite* length can occupy the second position. Then there are $2n - 2$ parts that can occupy position 3 while any one of the remaining $n - 1$ parts of the *opposite* length can occupy position 4, and so on. It follows that there are $(2n)(n)(2n - 2)(n - 1)(2n - 4)(n - 2) \cdot \cdots \cdot 4 \cdot 2 \cdot 2 \cdot 1$ ways of arranging the sticks in such a way that each new stick is composed of one long part and one short part. The probability is

$$\frac{(2n)(n)(2n - 2)(n - 1)(2n - 4)(n - 2) \cdot \cdots \cdot 4 \cdot 2 \cdot 2 \cdot 1}{(2n)(2n - 1)(2n - 2)(2n - 3)(2n - 4)(2n - 5) \cdot \cdots \cdot 4 \cdot 3 \cdot 2 \cdot 1}$$

$$= \frac{n!}{1 \cdot 3 \cdot 5 \cdot 7 \cdot \cdots \cdot (2n - 5)(2n - 3)(2n - 1)}.$$

Finally, we find the probability that each new stick is composed of either *two long parts* or *two short parts*. In this case, we observe that each pair of adjacent parts forming a new stick must be of the type *long-long* or *short-short*. Now there are *n*-pairs of parts and $C(n, n/2)$ ways of distributing the long-long pairs among the *n*-pairs. (Note that *n* is given as an even integer and so $n/2$ is an integer.) Within each distribution, the *n* long parts can appear in *n!* ways and the *n* short parts can also appear in *n!* ways. Therefore there are $C(n, n/2)(n!)^2$

ways of forming new sticks in such a way that each stick is composed of either two long parts or two short parts. The probability is

$$\frac{C(n, n/2)(n!)^2}{(2n)!}.$$

22.2 (a) This is a generalization of the counter problem from a coordinate *line* to a coordinate *plane*. In physics, this would be called a two-dimensional *random walk* problem. In this situation, there are 4 possible directions in which the counter can move on any one draw from the deck of cards. Consequently, when 8 cards are selected, there are 4^8 possible sequences of jumps in the plane. If we let R, L, U and D represent respectively a right, left, upward and downward jump in any sequence of jumps, then one sequence that takes the counter to the point $(1, 1)$ after 8 jumps is (U, D, R, L, D, U, R, U). If a few more such sequences are constructed, the student will observe that an arbitrary sequence of jumps taking the counter to the point $(1, 1)$ must satisfy certain conditions. If r, f, u and d represent respectively the number of right, left, upward and downward jumps in a sequence, then any sequence taking the counter to the point $(1, 1)$ in 8 jumps must satisfy the following conditions:

(a) $r \geq 1, u \geq 1$

(b) $r - f = 1$ and $u - d = 1$

(c) $r + f + u + d = 8$

Adding the two equations in condition (b), we obtain $r - f + u - d = 2$. Adding this equation to the one in condition (c), we arrive at $2r + 2u = 10$. This implies that $r + u = 5$ and, combining this result with conditions (a) and (b), we obtain only the following possible combinations of values for r, f, u and d:

1. $r = 1,$ $f = 0,$ $u = 4,$ $d = 3$
2. $r = 2,$ $f = 1,$ $u = 3,$ $d = 2$
3. $r = 3,$ $f = 2,$ $u = 2,$ $d = 1$
4. $r = 4,$ $f = 3,$ $u = 1,$ $d = 0$

Under combination 1, a sequence must have one R, no L's, 4 U's and 3 D's. The one R can go in any one of 8 positions in the sequence, and there are $C(7, 4)$ ways of using 4 U's in 4 of the other 7 positions with the 3 D's going into the remaining 3 positions in the sequence. Hence, there are $8 \cdot C(7, 4) = 280$ sequences under combination 1. A sequence under combination 2 must have 2 R's, 1 L, 3 U's and 2 D's. The one L can occupy any one of the 8 positions; the 2 R's can occupy any 2 of the remaining 7 positions in $C(7, 2)$ ways; the 3 U's can occupy any 3 of the remaining 5 positions in $C(5, 3)$ ways leaving the last 2 positions for the 2 D's. Hence there are $8 \cdot C(7, 2) \cdot C(5, 3) = 1680$ sequences under combination 2. Continuing as in the preceding combinations, we find that there are $8 \cdot C(7, 3) \cdot C(4, 2) = 1680$ sequences under combination 3 and $8 \cdot C(7, 4) = 280$ sequences under combination 4. It follows that there are $280 + 1680 + 1680 + 280 = 3920$ sequences that take the counter to the point $(1, 1)$ after 8 jumps, and so the corresponding probability is $3920/4^8$.

148

*Answers*_____

SECTION 1

1.6 (a) Yes (b) No (c) No (d) No
1.8 1. A, B, C, D, F 2. B, E 3. A, B, E 4. A, B, D, E 5. A 6. $A, B,$ C, D, F 7. A, B, C, D, E, F 8. B, E, G 9. B, D, E, F 10. B, E, G

SECTION 2

2.4 (a) 1 (b) 2 (c) 35
2.5 (a) 7 (b) 0 (c) 0

SECTION 3

3.1 $12 \cdot 1, 6 \cdot 2, 4 \cdot 3, 2 \cdot 6, 1 \cdot 12$
3.2 $72 \cdot 1, 36 \cdot 2, 24 \cdot 3, 18 \cdot 4, 12 \cdot 6, 9 \cdot 8, 6 \cdot 12, 4 \cdot 18, 3 \cdot 24, 2 \cdot 36,$ $1 \cdot 72$
3.3 (a) $q = 2, r = 11$ (b) $q = 1, r = 38$
      (c) $q = 9, r = 13$ (d) $q = 1, r = 140$
      (e) $q = 3, r = 247$ (f) $q = 4, r = 96$
3.4 (a) 0, 1, 2, 3, 4
      (b) 0, 1, 2, 3, 4, 5, 6
      (c) 0, 1

SECTION 4

4.1 $4935 = 4 \cdot 10^3 + 9 \cdot 10^2 + 3 \cdot 10 + 5$
      $33134 = 3 \cdot 10^4 + 3 \cdot 10^3 + 1 \cdot 10^2 + 3 \cdot 10 + 4$
      $71268 = 7 \cdot 10^4 + 1 \cdot 10^3 + 2 \cdot 10^2 + 6 \cdot 10 + 8$
      $71969 = 7 \cdot 10^4 + 1 \cdot 10^3 + 9 \cdot 10^2 + 6 \cdot 10 + 9$

4.2 $278 = (101022)_3$
$278 = (233)_{11}$
$278 = ([13][18])_{20} = (\text{XIII XVIII})_{20}$

4.3 $5243 = (131433)_5$
$5243 = (21200)_7$
$5243 = (1010001111011)_2$

4.4 $25276 = (61274)_8$
$25276 = (12764)_{12}$
$25276 = (7\ 1\ [16])_{60} = (7\ 1\ \text{XVI})_{60}$

4.5 $6 = (110)_2$
$28 = (11100)_2$
$496 = (111110000)_2$
$8128 = (1111111000000)_2$

4.9 (a) 8   (b) 125   (c) 1367
(d) 194   (e) 762   (f) 3454

4.10 (a) $x = 64$ (b) $y = 8$ (c) $z = 4$

4.11 (a) 1 red, 2 white, 4 blue, 6 green
(b) 2 red, 3 white, 5 blue, 7 green
(c) 5 red, 5 white, 5 blue, 5 green
(d) 7 red, 6 white, 5 blue, 4 green

4.12 (a) 11339 and 10512 seconds
(b) 2 hrs. 13 min. 20 sec. and 2 hrs. 58 min. 59 sec.

SECTION 5

5.1 (a) 7   (b) 19   (c) 22
(d) 53   (e) 1   (f) 41

5.2 (a) $(413)(2) + (273)(-3) = 7$
(b) $(171)(-3) + (133)(4) = 19$
(c) $(1034)(7) + (902)(-8) = 22$
(d) $(1643)(3) + (1219)(-4) = 53$

5.3 (a) $(57)(-3) + (43)(4) = 1$
(b) $(707)(-4) + (69)(41) = 1$
(c) $(1313)(88) + (227)(-509) = 1$
(d) $(1763)(-797) + (1739)(808) = 1$

5.5 (b) $(a + b, a - b) = 2$
(c) $(a + b, a - b) = 1$
(d) 1, 2

5.6 No; consider $(4)(2) + (6)(3) = 26$, $(4, 6) = 2 \neq 26$

5.7 (a) $x = -2, y = 5$; $x = 3, y = -7$. (There are other solutions.)
(b) $x = 27, y = -24$. (There are other solutions.)
(c) $x = 4, y = 2$; $x = 5, y = -1$. (There are other solutions.)

5.8 (a) $x = 1, y = -2$; $x = -4, y = 10$. (There are other solutions.)
(b) $x = 2, y = -6$; $x = -6, y = 24$. (There are other solutions.)

5.10. Integers x and y exist if and only if the greatest common divisor of a and b divides c.

SECTION 6

6.1 (a) 364   (b) 1105

6.2 (a) g.c.d. = 5, l.c.m. = 1105
(b) g.c.d. = 1, l.c.m. = $77 \cdot 221$
(c) g.c.d. = 14, l.c.m. = 364
(d) g.c.d. = 13, l.c.m. = $21 \cdot 1066 = 273 \cdot 82$

6.3 (a) 2964   (b) $97 \cdot 2101$
(c) $2233 \cdot 4199$ (d) $23 \cdot 4199 = 5083 \cdot 19$

6.4 (a) 243081657
(b) $9 \cdot 756910423$
(c) $3 \cdot 2976543123$

SECTION 7

7.1 (a) 6   (b) 6   (c) 1   (d) 1
(e) 6   (f) 6   (g) 3   (h) 3

7.2 (a) 5   (b) 5   (c) 10   (d) 10

7.3 (a) 12   (b) 12   (c) 3   (d) 3

7.4 (a) 15   (b) 15   (c) 5   (d) 5

7.5 (a) $S_{29} = \{1, 29\}$
(b) $S_{47} = \{1, 47\}$
(c) $S_p = \{1, p\}$

7.6 (a) $S_{21} = \{1, 3, 7, 21\}$
(b) $S_{35} = \{1, 5, 7, 35\}$
(c) $S_{pq} = \{1, p, q, pq\}$

7.7 All of the properties are satisfied except for the cancellation laws.

7.8 The integers under ordinary addition and multiplication satisfy only *one* distributive law and fail to satisfy properties (h) and (i). On the other hand, the integers satisfy the cancellation laws for addition and multiplication. Both systems satisfy properties (a), (b), (c) and (d).

SECTION 8

8.1 (a) $2^4 \cdot 31$ (b) $17 \cdot 59$
(c) 1009   (d) $2^6 \cdot 3^4$
(e) 5521   (f) $2^6 \cdot 127$
(g) $101 \cdot 103$ (h) 2^{16}
(i) $2^3 \cdot 5 \cdot 31 \cdot 131$ (j) $2^2 \cdot 5^3 \cdot 7^3$
(k) 2^{18} (l) $2^9 \cdot 3^6$

8.2 The expression yields a prime for all x with $1 \leq x \leq 40$, but it does not always yield a prime for values of x greater than 40; for example, it does not yield a prime when $x = 41$, $x = 42$, and $x = 45$. Can you find more values of x for which the expression is not a prime?

8.3   No, $2^{11} - 1 = 23 \cdot 89$

8.4   **(a)** 3, 4, 5, 6,   **(b)** 1   **(c)** 3

8.5   **(a)** All values except 1, 5 and 7.
          (b) All values except 7.
          (c) All values.

8.6   **(a)** 24—28; 32—36; 48—52
          (b) 90—96
          (c) 114—126 (thirteen); 200—210 (eleven)
          (d) For any positive integer n, let

$$(n + 1)! = (n + 1)(n)(n - 1)(n - 2) \cdot \cdots \cdot (3)(2)(1);$$

then the following sequence of numbers yields a set of n consecutive composite integers: $(n + 1)! + 2$, $(n + 1)! + 3$, $(n + 1)! + 4, \ldots, (n + 1)! + n$, $(n + 1)! + (n + 1)$.
For example, when $n = 6$ we obtain $7! + 2$, $7! + 3$, $7! + 4$, $7! + 5$, $7! + 6$, and $7! + 7$ as a set of 6 consecutive composite integers.

8.7   **(a)** 3 and 5, 5 and 7, 11 and 13, 17 and 19, 29 and 31, 41 and 43, 59 and 61, 71 and 73, 101 and 103, 107 and 109.
          (b) $p(p + 2) + 1 = p^2 + 2p + 1 = (p + 1)^2$. This result is true for any integers n and $n + 2$ since $n(n + 2) + 1 = (n + 1)^2$.
          (c) Nothing contradictory in the statements; since the integers form an infinite set, there is room for the truth of *both* statements.

8.8   **(a)** 5, 11, 17, 23, 19

8.9   **(a)** 7, 11, 19, 23, 31

8.10 **(a)** 7, 13, 19, 31, 37
          (b) 11, 17, 23, 29, 41

8.11 **(a)** $30 = 7 + 23 = 11 + 19 = 13 + 17$;
$40 = 3 + 37 = 11 + 29 = 17 + 23$;
$48 = 5 + 43 = 7 + 41 = 11 + 37 = 17 + 31 = 19 + 29$;
$102 = 5 + 97 = 13 + 89 = 19 + 83 = 23 + 79 =$
$29 + 73 = 31 + 71 = 41 + 61 = 43 + 59$;
$120 = 7 + 113 = 11 + 109 = 13 + 107 = 17 + 103$
$= 19 + 101 = 23 + 97 = 37 + 83 = 41 + 79$
$= 47 + 73 = 53 + 67 = 59 + 61$;
          (b) $27 = 3 + 5 + 19 = 3 + 7 + 17 = 3 + 11 + 13$
$= 5 + 5 + 17 = 5 + 11 + 11 = 7 + 7 + 13$;
$31 = 3 + 5 + 23 = 3 + 11 + 17 = 5 + 7 + 19$
$= 5 + 13 + 13 = 7 + 7 + 17 = 7 + 11 + 13$;
$63 = 3 + 7 + 53 = 3 + 13 + 47 = 3 + 17 + 43$
$= 3 + 19 + 41 = 3 + 23 + 37 = 3 + 29 + 31$
$= 5 + 5 + 53 = 5 + 11 + 47 = 5 + 17 + 41$
$= 5 + 29 + 29 = 7 + 13 + 43 = 7 + 19 + 37$
$= 11 + 23 + 29 = 13 + 13 + 37 = 13 + 19 + 31$
$= 17 + 17 + 29 = 17 + 23 + 23$.

8.12 **(a)** $496 = 2^4 \cdot 31$; the other factorizations are:
2, 2^2, 2^3, 2^4, 31, $2 \cdot 31$, $2^2 \cdot 31$, $2^3 \cdot 31$

(b) $360 = 2^3 \cdot 3^2 \cdot 5$; the other factorizations are:
$2, 2^2, 2^3, 3, 3^2, 5, 2 \cdot 3, 2 \cdot 3^2, 2 \cdot 5, 2^2 \cdot 3, 2^2 \cdot 3^2, 2^2 \cdot 5, 2^3 \cdot 3,$
$2^3 \cdot 3^2, \ 2^3 \cdot 5, \ 3 \cdot 5, \ 3^2 \cdot 5, \ 2 \cdot 3 \cdot 5, \ 2 \cdot 3^2 \cdot 5, \ 2^2 \cdot 3 \cdot 5,$
$2^2 \cdot 3^2 \cdot 5, 2^3 \cdot 3 \cdot 5$

8.13 (a) $(600, 4500) = 300$, $[600, 4500] = 9000$; the standard factorizations are: $600 = 2^3 \cdot 3 \cdot 5^2$, $4500 = 2^2 \cdot 3^2 \cdot 5^3$, $300 = 2^2 \cdot 3 \cdot 5^2$, $9000 = 2^3 \cdot 3^2 \cdot 5^3$

(b) $(504, 540) = 36$, $[504, 540] = 7560$; the standard factorizations are: $504 = 2^3 \cdot 3^2 \cdot 7$, $540 = 2^2 \cdot 3^3 \cdot 5$, $36 = 2^2 \cdot 3^2$, $7560 = 2^3 \cdot 3^3 \cdot 5 \cdot 7$

8.14 (a) No

(b) 2, 6, 10, 14, 18, 22, 26, 30, 34, 38

(c) $16 = 2 \cdot 8$
$20 = 2 \cdot 10$
$30 = 30$
$36 = 2 \cdot 18$
$40 = 2 \cdot 20$
$50 = 50$
$60 = 2 \cdot 30$
$140 = 2 \cdot 70$

(d) $16 = 2 \cdot 8 = 4 \cdot 4$
$36 = 2 \cdot 18 = 6 \cdot 6$
$40 = 2 \cdot 20 = 4 \cdot 10$
$60 = 2 \cdot 30 = 6 \cdot 10$
$140 = 2 \cdot 70 = 10 \cdot 14$

SECTION 9

9.1 (a) 10 (b) 2 (c) 45
(d) 14 (e) 54 (f) 144

9.2 The positive divisors of 496 are: $1, 2, 2^2, 2^3, 2^4, 31, 2 \cdot 31, 2^2 \cdot 31,$ $2^3 \cdot 31, 2^4 \cdot 31 = 496$. The positive divisors of 8128 are: $1, 2, 2^2, 2^3,$ $2^4, 2^5, 2^6, 127, 2 \cdot 127, 2^2 \cdot 127, 2^3 \cdot 127, 2^4 \cdot 127, 2^5 \cdot 127, 2^6 \cdot 127 =$ 8128.

9.3 (a) $2^6 = 64$ (b) $2^2 \cdot 3 = 12$
(c) $2^3 \cdot 3 = 24$ (d) 2^{96}

9.4 (a) 9 (b) 12 (c) 10

9.5 (a) $((12)(45))^* = 24 < 36 = (12)^* (45)^*$
(b) Any pair of positive integers a and b that are not relatively prime will work.

9.6 (c) Any pair of relatively prime integers will work.
(e) Yes

9.7 (a) 4 (b) 6 (c) 144 (d) 48

SECTION 10

10.1 $(a, b) = 2^3 \cdot 3^3 \cdot 13^3 \cdot 19 \cdot 23^2$
$[a, b] = 2^5 \cdot 3^4 \cdot 5^2 \cdot 7^2 \cdot 11^2 \cdot 13^4 \cdot 19^2 \cdot 23^4 \cdot 29^3 \cdot 31$

10.2 **(a)** 180 and 5400
     (b) 1 and (6368)(7623)
     (c) 77 and (143)(45815) or (11011)(595)
     (d) 1 and (6368)(11011)

10.3 **(a)** 1 and (2233)(4199)
     (b) 221 and (23)(4199) or (19)(5083)
     (c) 53 and (23)(1643) or (31)(1219)
     (d) 1 and (413)(16278)
     (e) 41 and (173)(13489) or (329)(7093)

SECTION 11

11.1 **(a)** $2^{22} \cdot 3^2 \cdot 5^2$
     (b) $2^2 \cdot 5^2 \cdot 7 \cdot 37$
     (c) $2^{2 \cdot 3} \cdot 5^2 \cdot 233$
     (d) $2^{2^{2} \cdot 3}$
     (e) $2^2 \cdot 3 \cdot 5 \cdot 13 \cdot 73$
     (f) $2^3 \cdot 3^2 \cdot 5^2 \cdot 101$

11.2 **(a)** $2^{2 \cdot 3} \cdot 6221$
     (b) $2^3 \cdot 3^2 \cdot 5^2 \cdot 173$
     (c) $2^{22} \cdot 3 \cdot 5 \cdot 31 \cdot 101$
     (d) $2^{2 \cdot 3} \cdot 3 \cdot 5 \cdot 23 \cdot 47$
     (e) $2^{2^{2} \cdot 3^2 \cdot 5^2}$

11.3 **(a)** $5 \cdot 7, 5^7, 7^5$
     (b) $5^5 \cdot 7, 5 \cdot 7^5, 5^{5 \cdot 7}, 5^{5^7}, 5^{7^5}, 7^{5^5}$
     (c) $5^{5^{7^7}}, 5^{7^{5^7}}, 5^{7^{7^5}}, 7^{5^{5^7}}, 7^{5^{7^5}}, 7^{7^{5^5}}, 5^{7^{5 \cdot 7}}, 7^{5^{5 \cdot 7}}, 5^{5^{7 \cdot 7}}, 7^{5^{5 \cdot 7}}, 7^{5^{5 \cdot 7}}, 7^{5 \cdot 7^5},$
         $5^{5^7} \cdot 7, 5^{7^5} \cdot 7, 5 \cdot 7^{5^7}, 5 \cdot 7^{7^5}, 5^5 \cdot 7^7, 5^7 \cdot 7^5, 5 \cdot 7^{5 \cdot 7}, 5^{5 \cdot 7} \cdot 7$
     (d) $3 \cdot 5 \cdot 7, 3^7 \cdot 5, 3 \cdot 5^7, 3^5 \cdot 7, 3 \cdot 7^5, 5^3 \cdot 7, 5 \cdot 7^3, 3^{5 \cdot 7}, 5^{3 \cdot 7},$
         $7^{3 \cdot 5}, 3^{5^7}, 3^{7^5}, 5^{3^7}, 5^{7^3}, 7^{3^5}, 7^{5^3}$
     (e) $5^{5^{5^{5^5}}}$

11.4 **(a)** 455625
     (b) 3,359,232
     (c) 4096
     (d) 43,046,721
     (e) 20736

11.5 **(a)** 480
     (b) 10360
     (c) 27960
     (d) 48
     (e) 56940
     (f) 36360

11.6 **(a)** 12, 18, 64, 81, 256, 512
     (b) 24, 54, 3^6, 3^8, 3^9, 2^{27}

(c) $36, 48, 162, 2^{12}, 2^{18}, 2^{64}, 2^{81}, 2^{256}, 2^{512}, 3^{16}$

(d) $2^{2^{27}}, 2^{3^{8}}, 2^{3^{9}}, 3^{256}, 3^{512}, 3^{81}, 2^{729}, 3^{64}, 2^{24}, 2^{54}, 3^{12}, 3^{18}, 768,$
     $1536, 13122, 39366, 108, 72, 1458, 192$

11.7   (a) $2^{2^{2^{2}}}$

       (b) $2 \cdot 5 \cdot 7, \ 2^{7} \cdot 5, \ 2 \cdot 5^{7}, \ 2^{5} \cdot 7, \ 2 \cdot 7^{5}, \ 5^{2} \cdot 7, \ 5 \cdot 7^{2}, \ 2^{5 \cdot 7},$
           $5^{2 \cdot 7}, \ 7^{2 \cdot 5}, \ 2^{5^{7}}, \ 2^{7^{5}}, \ 5^{2^{7}}, \ 5^{7^{2}}, \ 7^{2^{5}}, \ 7^{5^{2}}$

11.8   (a) $pq, \ p^{q}, \ q^{p}$

       (b) $p^{q} \cdot q, \ pq^{q}, \ q^{p \ q}, \ p^{q^{q}}, \ q^{p^{q}}, \ q^{q^{p}}$

       (c) $pqr, \ p^{r} \cdot q, \ pq^{r}, \ p^{q} \cdot r, \ pr^{q}, \ q^{p} \cdot r, \ qr^{p}, \ p^{qr}, \ q^{pr}, \ r^{pq}, \ p^{q^{r}}, \ p^{r^{q}},$
           $q^{p^{r}}, \ q^{r^{p}}, \ r^{p^{q}}, \ r^{q^{p}}$

11.10   (a)   48   (b)   241   (c)   1524

11.11   (a) $150 < 576$

       (b) $a = 6, b = 9$; there are infinitely many other choices for a and b.

11.12   (a) $34 > 32$

       (b) $a = 2, \ b = 2^{32}$; there are infinitely many other choices for a and b.

11.13   (a) $630 = 630$

       (b) $120 = 120$

       (c)   Choose any two numbers a and b with a and b relatively prime.

       (d)   Appendix

       (e)   No; try $a = 2$ and $b = 6$ (see Appendix).

11.14   There are 6^{4} mosaics that can be made by using five distinct primes and there are $(k + 1)^{k-1}$ mosaics that can be made using k distinct primes.

SECTION 12

12.1   (a)   The student should be able to find the divisors from the following standard factorizations:

$$120 = 2^{3} \cdot 3 \cdot 5$$
$$1116 = 2^{2} \cdot 3^{2} \cdot 31$$
$$2^{10}(2^{11} - 1) = 2^{10}(2047) = 2^{10} \cdot 23 \cdot 89$$

       (b)   8, 9, 10, 14, 15, 16, 21

       (c)   12, 18, 20, 24, 30, 36, 40

12.2   (a)   No, there is no perfect number between 10^{4} and 10^{5}

       (b)   No, the fifth and sixth perfect numbers end in 6

12.6   The student should be able to find the divisors from the standard factorizations:

$$120 = 2^{3} \cdot 3 \cdot 5$$
$$672 = 2^{5} \cdot 3 \cdot 7$$
$$30240 = 2^{5} \cdot 3^{3} \cdot 5 \cdot 7$$

12.7   (b)   10, 19, 91, 82, 37, 73, 46, 64, 55, 100; there are infinitely many others

12.9   (a) 2^{4} (b) $2^{6} \cdot 31 \cdot 127$ (c)   10, 14   (d)   44

12.10 (a) 2^{q-1} (b) $2^{p-1}(2^p - 1)(2^q - 1)$ (c) $2p, 2q$
  (d) $4(p + q - 1)$ (e) 76

12.11 (b) Perfect numbers occur when $n = 1, 2, 3,$ and 6.
  (c) Every even perfect number except 6 has the same form as the expression given in (a) with $2n + 1$ equal to a prime p and $2n = p - 1$.

12.12 (a) $6 = (110)_2$
    $28 = (11100)_2$
    $496 = (111110000)_2$
    $8128 = (1111111000000)_2$
  (b) $(\overbrace{111 \ldots 11}^{2n+1 \text{ ones}}\overbrace{000 \ldots 00}^{2n \text{ zeros}})_2$
  (c) $28 = (130)_4$
    $496 = (13300)_4$
    $8128 = (1333000)_4$
  (d) $2^{2n}(2^{2n+1} - 1) = (\overbrace{133 \ldots 3}^{n \text{ threes}}\overbrace{00 \ldots 0}^{n \text{ zeros}})_4$
  (e) $33550336 = (1\,3\,3\,3\,3\,3\,3\,0\,0\,0\,0\,0\,0)_4$

12.13 (a) 168 (b) 403

  (c) 1170 (d) $\dfrac{p^{i+1} - 1}{p - 1}$

  (e) $\dfrac{p^{i+1} - 1}{p - 1} \cdot \dfrac{q^{i+1} - 1}{q - 1}$

  (f) $\dfrac{p^{i+1} - 1}{p - 1} \cdot \dfrac{q^{i+1} - 1}{q - 1} \cdot \dfrac{r^{k+1} - 1}{r - 1}$

12.14 (a) $124 < 144$
  (b) Any two integers a and b that are *not* relatively prime.

12.15 (a) $403 = 403$
  (b) $560 = 560$
  (c) Any two integers a and b that are relatively prime.
  (e) Yes

SECTION 13

13.1 (a) 0 (b) 0 (c) 5 (d) 0
13.2 (a) 6 (b) 1 (c) 3 (d) 6
13.5 (a) Yes (b) No
13.6 (d) 3, 4
13.7 (d) 1, 1
13.8 (a) Yes (b) No
13.9 Interpret $a - b$ as follows: start at a on the clock dial, go b units in the counter-clockwise direction. In the modulo-six system, $5 - 3 = 2$ and $3 - 5 = 4$. In the modulo-seven system, $5 - 3 = 2$ and $3 - 5 = 5$.

13.10 $\sqrt{0} = 0$, $\sqrt{1} = 1$ and 4, $\sqrt{4} = 2$ and 3, and $\sqrt{2}$ and $\sqrt{3}$ do not exist.

13.11 $\sqrt[3]{0} = 0$, $\sqrt[3]{1} = 1$, $\sqrt[3]{2} = 3$, $\sqrt[3]{3} = 2$, $\sqrt[3]{4} = 4$

13.12 (a) 3   (b) 4

13.13 (a) 0   (b) 0

13.14 (a) 0   (b) 0

13.15 (a) 4   (b) 6

13.16 (a) 3:00 AM   (b) 1:00 AM   (c) 5:00 PM

13.17 (a) Thursday   (b) Tuesday   (c) Saturday

13.18 (a) December   (b) December   (c) January

SECTION 14

14.3 (a) 4, 0, 2   (b) 0, 0, 0   (c) 6, 4, 0

14.5 (a) In R_9 : 3, 2, 8.   In R_{11} : 1, 2, 2
 (b) In R_{15} : 9, 13, 8.   In R_{17} : 7, 15, 7
 (c) In R_{15} : 10, 14, 6.   In R_{19} : 6, 18, 4
 (d) In R_{47} : 31, 43, 13.   In R_{59} : 19, 55, 42
 (e) In R_{33} : 3, 8, 11.   In R_{55} : 36, 8, 33

14.6 (a)

	R_7	R_8	R_{10}	R_{11}	R_{12}	R_{13}
$\sqrt{3}$	none	none	none	5, 6	none	4, 9
$\sqrt{4}$	2, 5	2, 6	2, 8	2, 9	2, 4, 8, 10	2, 11
$\sqrt{5}$	none	none	5	4, 7	none	none
$\sqrt{6}$	none	none	4, 6	none	none	none
$\sqrt[3]{3}$	none	none	7	9	3	none
$\sqrt[3]{4}$	none	none	4	5	4, 10	none
$\sqrt[3]{5}$	none	5, 7	5	3	5	7, 8, 11
$\sqrt[3]{6}$	3, 5, 6	none	6	8	none	none

(c)

	R_5	R_7	R_{10}	R_{11}	R_{12}
$\sqrt{1}$	1, 4	1, 6	1, 9	1, 10	1, 5, 7, 11
$\sqrt{-1}$	2, 3	none	3, 7	none	none

14.7 (a) Let $x = 2$, $y = 1$, $z = 1$, or let $x = 2$, $y = 4$, $z = 6$. There are other solutions.
 (b) Let $x = 6$, $y = 1$, $z = 1$, or let $x = 6$, $y = 2$, $z = 2$. There are other solutions.

SECTION 15

15.1   **(a)**   6, 0, does not exist, 2, 6
        (b)   2, 5, 0, 8, 2
        (c)   does not exist, 1, does not exist, 6, does not exist

15.2   **(a)**   4, does not exist, 3, 1, 9
        (b)   does not exist, 6, 10, does not exist, 7
        (c)   6, does not exist, 10, does not exist, 2
        (d)   7, 2, 10, 4, 8
        (e)   3, does not exist, 6, 9, 2

15.4   **(a)**   In R_9, 5; in R_{11}, 8.
        (b)   In R_{15}, 2; in R_{17}, 10.
        (c)   In R_{15}, 9; in R_{19}, 17.
        (d)   In R_{47}, 33; in R_{59}, 34.
        (e)   In R_{33}, 11; in R_{55}, 33.
        (f)   In R_{139}, 77; in R_{161}, does not exist.

15.5   **(a)**   Yes   **(b)**   No   **(c)**   Yes   **(d)**   No   **(e)**   Yes

15.12   **(a)**   In R_7, 6; in R_8, 7; in R_{11}, 10.
        (b)   In R_7, 1; in R_8, none; in R_{11}, 1.

15.13   **(a)** $n - 1$ **(b)**   1   **(c)**   No

15.14   **(a)**   Zero in each system.
        (b)   2, 4, 5, 6

15.15   **(a)**   Zero in each system.
        (b)   4, 6, 10, 12

15.16   **(a)**   In R_4, 0 and 2; in R_5, 0; in R_7, 0; in R_8, 0 and 4; in R_9, 0; in R_{11}, 0; in R_{12}, 0 and 6.
        (b)   No
        (c)   In R_{13}, no; in R_{14}, yes.
        (d)   In R_{33}, no; in R_{56}, yes.

15.18   **(a)**   In R_4, 3; in R_5, 4; in R_6, 5; in R_7, 6; in R_8, 1; in R_9, 8; in R_{10}, 9; in R_{11}, 10; in R_{12}, 1.
        (b)   In R_{17}, yes; in R_{19}, no.

SECTION 16

16.1   **(a)** $x = 3$ **(b)** $x = 6$ **(c)** $x = 1$

16.2   **(a)** $x = 3$ **(b)** $x = 1$ and 5   **(c)** $x = 4$
        (d)   no solutions

16.3   **(a)** $x = 2$ **(b)** $x = 5$ **(c)** $x = 1$

16.4   **(a)** $x = 2$ and 8   **(b)**   no solution
        (c) $x = 1$ **(d)** $x = 5$

16.5   **(a)** $x = 19$ **(b)**   no solution
        (c)   no solution   **(d)** $x = 17$

16.6   In R_3, $x = 2$; in R_5, $x = 1$; in R_8, $x = 6$.

16.7 In R_5, $x = 1$; in R_7, no solution; in R_{11}, $x = 2$ and 6.

16.8 In R_{10}, $x = 3$ and 8; in R_{12}, $x = 1$ and 10.

16.9 In R_{11}, $x = 2$ and 4, in R_{13}, no solution.

16.10 In R_8, $x = 1, 3, 5,$ and 7; in R_9, $x = 6$ and 8.

16.11 (a) $x = 4, 7, 8,$ and 11
       (b) $x = 2, 4, 8,$ and 10
       (c) no solution
       (d) $x = 0, 2, 3, 5, 6, 8, 9,$ and 11

16.12 (a) $x = 5$ and 6   (b) $x = 3$ and 12

16.13 (a) $x = 5$ and 13   (b) $x = 3$ and 13

16.14 (a) $x = 7$ and 12   (b) $x = 9$ and 12

16.15 (a) In R_7, $x = 2, 4$ and 6; in R_8, $x = 7$.

16.16 (a) $(x - 2)(x - 4)$ (b) $(x - 3)(x - 9)$
       (c) $(x - 7)(6x + 2)$ (d) $3(x - 3)(x - 3)$
       (e) $(x - 8)(x - 8)$ (f) $(x - 3)(3x + 13)$ or $(x - 9)(3x + 1)$

16.17 (a) $(x - 6)(x - 7)$, $(x - 1)(x - 2)$
       (b) $(x - 6)(x - 11)$, $(x - 2)(x - 3)$
       (c) $(x - 8)(3x + 13)$, $(x - 14)(3x + 1)$
       (d) $(x - 4)(x - 10)$, $(x - 2)(x - 12)$
       (e) $(x - 6)(x - 11)$, $(x - 18)(x - 20)$
       (f) $4x(x + 1)$, $4x(x - 5)$, $4(x - 2)(x - 9)$, $4(x - 3)(x - 8)$,
           $(x - 2)(x - 6)$, $4(x - 2)(x - 3)$, $4(x - 3)(x - 5)$,
           $4(x - 5)(x - 6)$

SECTION 17

17.1 (a) $\begin{pmatrix} 4 & 3 \\ 3 & -4 \end{pmatrix}$ (b) $\begin{pmatrix} 3 & -2 \\ 5 & 5 \end{pmatrix}$ (c) $\begin{pmatrix} -1 & 5 \\ 2 & 3 \end{pmatrix}$

17.2 (a) $\begin{pmatrix} 4 & 3 \\ 3 & 3 \end{pmatrix}$ (b) $\begin{pmatrix} 3 & 5 \\ 5 & 5 \end{pmatrix}$ (c) $\begin{pmatrix} 6 & 5 \\ 2 & 3 \end{pmatrix}$

17.3 (a) $\begin{pmatrix} 4 & 3 \\ 3 & 9 \end{pmatrix}$ (b) $\begin{pmatrix} 3 & 11 \\ 5 & 5 \end{pmatrix}$ (c) $\begin{pmatrix} 12 & 5 \\ 2 & 3 \end{pmatrix}$

17.4 (a) The additive inverses are $\begin{pmatrix} -1 & -5 \\ -2 & 4 \end{pmatrix}$ and $\begin{pmatrix} -3 & 2 \\ -1 & 0 \end{pmatrix}$. The differ-
       ence of the matrices is $\begin{pmatrix} -2 & 7 \\ 1 & -4 \end{pmatrix}$.

       (b) The additive inverses are $\begin{pmatrix} 3 & 0 \\ -2 & -4 \end{pmatrix}$ and $\begin{pmatrix} -6 & 2 \\ -3 & -1 \end{pmatrix}$. The dif-
       ference of the matrices is $\begin{pmatrix} -9 & 2 \\ -1 & 3 \end{pmatrix}$.

(c) The additive inverses are $\begin{pmatrix} 5 & -2 \\ -3 & -1 \end{pmatrix}$ and $\begin{pmatrix} -4 & -3 \\ 1 & -2 \end{pmatrix}$. The difference of the matrices is $\begin{pmatrix} -9 & -1 \\ 4 & -1 \end{pmatrix}$.

17.5 (a) The additive inverses are $\begin{pmatrix} 6 & 2 \\ 5 & 4 \end{pmatrix}$ and $\begin{pmatrix} 4 & 2 \\ 6 & 0 \end{pmatrix}$. The difference of the matrices is $\begin{pmatrix} 5 & 0 \\ 1 & 3 \end{pmatrix}$.

(b) The additive inverses are $\begin{pmatrix} 3 & 0 \\ 5 & 3 \end{pmatrix}$ and $\begin{pmatrix} 1 & 2 \\ 4 & 6 \end{pmatrix}$. The difference of the matrices is $\begin{pmatrix} 5 & 2 \\ 6 & 3 \end{pmatrix}$.

(c) The additive inverses are $\begin{pmatrix} 5 & 5 \\ 4 & 6 \end{pmatrix}$ and $\begin{pmatrix} 3 & 4 \\ 1 & 5 \end{pmatrix}$. The difference of the matrices is $\begin{pmatrix} 5 & 6 \\ 4 & 6 \end{pmatrix}$.

17.6 (a) The additive inverses are $\begin{pmatrix} 12 & 8 \\ 11 & 4 \end{pmatrix}$ and $\begin{pmatrix} 10 & 2 \\ 12 & 0 \end{pmatrix}$. The difference of the matrices is $\begin{pmatrix} 11 & 7 \\ 1 & 9 \end{pmatrix}$.

(b) The additive inverses are $\begin{pmatrix} 3 & 0 \\ 11 & 9 \end{pmatrix}$ and $\begin{pmatrix} 7 & 2 \\ 10 & 12 \end{pmatrix}$. The difference of the matrices is $\begin{pmatrix} 4 & 2 \\ 12 & 3 \end{pmatrix}$.

(c) The additive inverses are $\begin{pmatrix} 5 & 11 \\ 10 & 12 \end{pmatrix}$ and $\begin{pmatrix} 9 & 10 \\ 1 & 11 \end{pmatrix}$. The difference of the matrices is $\begin{pmatrix} 4 & 12 \\ 4 & 12 \end{pmatrix}$.

17.7 (a) $\begin{pmatrix} 8 & -2 \\ 2 & -4 \end{pmatrix}$ (b) $\begin{pmatrix} -18 & 6 \\ 24 & 0 \end{pmatrix}$ (c) $\begin{pmatrix} -22 & -11 \\ 11 & 11 \end{pmatrix}$

17.8 (a) In R_7, the products are $\begin{pmatrix} 1 & 5 \\ 2 & 3 \end{pmatrix}$, $\begin{pmatrix} 3 & 6 \\ 3 & 0 \end{pmatrix}$, $\begin{pmatrix} 6 & 3 \\ 4 & 4 \end{pmatrix}$.

(b) In R_{13}, the products are $\begin{pmatrix} 8 & 11 \\ 2 & 9 \end{pmatrix}$, $\begin{pmatrix} 8 & 6 \\ 11 & 0 \end{pmatrix}$, $\begin{pmatrix} 4 & 2 \\ 11 & 11 \end{pmatrix}$.

17.9 (a) In R_{11}, the products are $\begin{pmatrix} 8 & 9 \\ 2 & 7 \end{pmatrix}$, $\begin{pmatrix} 4 & 6 \\ 2 & 0 \end{pmatrix}$, $\begin{pmatrix} 0 & 0 \\ 0 & 0 \end{pmatrix}$.

(b) In R_8, the products are $\begin{pmatrix} 0 & 6 \\ 2 & 4 \end{pmatrix}$, $\begin{pmatrix} 6 & 6 \\ 0 & 0 \end{pmatrix}$, $\begin{pmatrix} 2 & 5 \\ 3 & 3 \end{pmatrix}$.

17.10 (a) Yes (b) Yes, $\begin{pmatrix} 1 & 1 \\ 1 & 1 \end{pmatrix}$

(c) A has a multiplicative inverse if and only if each of the entries a, b, c, and d are not zero.

(d)   Yes. Let $A = \begin{pmatrix} 1 & 0 \\ 0 & 1 \end{pmatrix}$, $B = \begin{pmatrix} 0 & 1 \\ 1 & 0 \end{pmatrix}$.

17.11   Any matrix of the type $\begin{pmatrix} 0 & a \\ 0 & 0 \end{pmatrix}$ or $\begin{pmatrix} 0 & 0 \\ a & 0 \end{pmatrix}$ where a is a nonzero integer.

17.12 $\begin{pmatrix} 1 & 0 \\ 0 & 0 \end{pmatrix}$, $\begin{pmatrix} 0 & 0 \\ 0 & 1 \end{pmatrix}$, $\begin{pmatrix} 1/2 & 1/2 \\ 1/2 & 1/2 \end{pmatrix}$ all satisfy the given condition.

17.13 $k = 4$

17.14   **(a)** $A^n = \begin{pmatrix} 2^{n-1} & 2^{n-1} \\ 2^{n-1} & 2^{n-1} \end{pmatrix}$

   (b) $A^n = \begin{pmatrix} 0 & 0 \\ 0 & 0 \end{pmatrix}$

SECTION 18

18.1   **(a)** $\begin{pmatrix} 2/7 & 5/14 \\ 1/7 & -1/14 \end{pmatrix}$, $\begin{pmatrix} 0 & 1 \\ -1/2 & 3/2 \end{pmatrix}$

   (b) $\begin{pmatrix} -1/3 & 0 \\ 1/6 & 1/4 \end{pmatrix}$, $\begin{pmatrix} 1/12 & 1/6 \\ -1/4 & 1/2 \end{pmatrix}$

   (c) $\begin{pmatrix} -1/11 & 2/11 \\ 3/11 & 5/11 \end{pmatrix}$, $\begin{pmatrix} 2/11 & -3/11 \\ 1/11 & 4/11 \end{pmatrix}$

18.2   In R_7, the multiplicative inverses are:

   (a)   does not exist, $\begin{pmatrix} 0 & 1 \\ 3 & 5 \end{pmatrix}$

   (b) $\begin{pmatrix} 2 & 0 \\ 6 & 2 \end{pmatrix}$, $\begin{pmatrix} 3 & 6 \\ 5 & 4 \end{pmatrix}$

   (c) $\begin{pmatrix} 5 & 4 \\ 6 & 3 \end{pmatrix}$, $\begin{pmatrix} 4 & 1 \\ 2 & 1 \end{pmatrix}$.

   In R_{13}, the multiplicative inverses are:

   (a) $\begin{pmatrix} 4 & 5 \\ 2 & 12 \end{pmatrix}$, $\begin{pmatrix} 0 & 1 \\ 6 & 8 \end{pmatrix}$

   (b) $\begin{pmatrix} 4 & 0 \\ 11 & 10 \end{pmatrix}$, $\begin{pmatrix} 12 & 11 \\ 3 & 7 \end{pmatrix}$

   (c) $\begin{pmatrix} 7 & 12 \\ 5 & 4 \end{pmatrix}$, $\begin{pmatrix} 12 & 8 \\ 6 & 11 \end{pmatrix}$.

18.3   In R_{11}, the additive inverses are:

   (a) $\begin{pmatrix} 10 & 6 \\ 9 & 4 \end{pmatrix}$, $\begin{pmatrix} 8 & 2 \\ 10 & 0 \end{pmatrix}$

(b) $\begin{pmatrix} 3 & 0 \\ 9 & 7 \end{pmatrix}, \begin{pmatrix} 5 & 2 \\ 8 & 10 \end{pmatrix}$

(c) $\begin{pmatrix} 5 & 9 \\ 8 & 10 \end{pmatrix}, \begin{pmatrix} 7 & 8 \\ 1 & 9 \end{pmatrix}$.

In R_{11}, the multiplicative inverses are:

(a) $\begin{pmatrix} 5 & 9 \\ 8 & 7 \end{pmatrix}, \begin{pmatrix} 0 & 1 \\ 5 & 7 \end{pmatrix}$

(b) $\begin{pmatrix} 7 & 0 \\ 2 & 3 \end{pmatrix}, \begin{pmatrix} 1 & 2 \\ 8 & 6 \end{pmatrix}$

(c) does not exist, does not exist.

In R_8, the additive inverses are:

(a) $\begin{pmatrix} 7 & 3 \\ 6 & 4 \end{pmatrix}, \begin{pmatrix} 5 & 2 \\ 7 & 0 \end{pmatrix}$

(b) $\begin{pmatrix} 3 & 0 \\ 6 & 4 \end{pmatrix}, \begin{pmatrix} 2 & 2 \\ 5 & 7 \end{pmatrix}$

(c) $\begin{pmatrix} 5 & 6 \\ 5 & 7 \end{pmatrix}, \begin{pmatrix} 4 & 5 \\ 1 & 6 \end{pmatrix}$.

In R_8, the multiplicative inverses are:
(a) does not exist, does not exist
(b) does not exist, does not exist

(c) $\begin{pmatrix} 5 & 6 \\ 1 & 7 \end{pmatrix}, \begin{pmatrix} 6 & 7 \\ 3 & 4 \end{pmatrix}$.

18.5 (a) There are 16 matrices in this set.

(b) $\begin{pmatrix} 1 & 0 \\ 0 & 1 \end{pmatrix}, \begin{pmatrix} 0 & 1 \\ 1 & 0 \end{pmatrix}, \begin{pmatrix} 1 & 1 \\ 1 & 0 \end{pmatrix}, \begin{pmatrix} 1 & 1 \\ 0 & 1 \end{pmatrix}, \begin{pmatrix} 1 & 0 \\ 1 & 1 \end{pmatrix}, \begin{pmatrix} 0 & 1 \\ 1 & 1 \end{pmatrix}$

18.7 (a) $\begin{pmatrix} -5/2 & 17/2 \\ 2 & -4 \end{pmatrix}$ (b) $\begin{pmatrix} -1/4 & -1/2 \\ -5/6 & 7/3 \end{pmatrix}$

(c) $\begin{pmatrix} -8/11 & 23/11 \\ 7/11 & -5/11 \end{pmatrix}$

18.8 In R_7, the quotients are:

(a) $\begin{pmatrix} 1 & 5 \\ 2 & 3 \end{pmatrix}$ (b) $\begin{pmatrix} 5 & 3 \\ 5 & 0 \end{pmatrix}$ (c) $\begin{pmatrix} 5 & 4 \\ 0 & 4 \end{pmatrix}$.

In R_{13}, the quotients are:

(a) $\begin{pmatrix} 4 & 2 \\ 2 & 9 \end{pmatrix}$ (b) $\begin{pmatrix} 3 & 6 \\ 10 & 11 \end{pmatrix}$ (c) $\begin{pmatrix} 4 & 8 \\ 3 & 9 \end{pmatrix}$.

In R_8, the quotients are:

(a) does not exist   **(b)** does not exist

(c) $\begin{pmatrix} 0 & 5 \\ 5 & 1 \end{pmatrix}$.

SECTION 19

19.1 **(a)** 3/12   **(b)** 3/12   **(c)** 7/12   **(d)** 4/12   **(e)** 1/12
      (f) 2/12   **(g)** 3/12   **(h)** 3/12   **(i)** 5/12

19.2 **(a)** 24/132   **(b)** 12/132   **(c)** 6/132   **(d)** 12/132
      (e) 2/132

19.3 **(a)** 6/36   **(b)** 3/36   **(c)** 4/36   **(d)** 27/36   **(e)** 9/36
      (f) 9/36   **(g)** 18/36   **(h)** 27/36   **(i)** 18/36

19.4 **(a)** 12/2652   **(b)** 132/2652   **(c)** 156/2652
      (d) 2028/2652

19.5 **(a)** 24/132600   **(b)** 1320/132600
      (c) 1716/132600   **(d)** 52728/132600

19.6 **(a)** $(4/52)^2$ **(b)** $(12/52)^2$ **(c)** $(13/52)^2$ **(d)** $\dfrac{(52)(39)}{(52)^2}$

19.7 **(a)** $(4/52)^3$ **(b)** $(12/52)^3$ **(c)** $(13/52)^3$ **(d)** $\dfrac{(52)(39)(26)}{(52)^3}$

19.8 **(a)** 1/37   **(b)** 18/37   **(c)** 18/37   **(d)** 9/37
      (e) 9/37   **(f)** 5/37   **(g)** 5/37   **(h)** 12/37
      (i) 7/37   **(j)** 11/37   **(k)** 5/37   **(l)** 4/37
      (m) 1/37

19.9 **(a)** $(18/37)^2$ **(b)** $(11/37)^2$ **(c)** $2(18/37)^2$
      (d) $2(18/37)^2$ **(e)** $16/(37)^2$ **(f)** $8/(37)^2$

19.10 **(a)** $(18/37)^3$ **(b)** $3(18/37)^3$ **(c)** $\dfrac{(6)(18)^2}{(37)^3}$

      (d) $(9/37)^3$ **(e)** $3(18/37)^3$ **(f)** $28/(37)^3$
      (g) $27/(37)^3$ **(h)** $54/(37)^3$

SECTION 20

20.1 **(a)** $5/2^5$ **(b)** 0   **(c)** $15/2^6$

20.2 **(a)** $56/2^8$ **(b)** $8/2^8$ **(c)** 0   **(d)** $10/2^5$

20.3 **(a)** 6/21   **(b)** 4/21   **(c)** 10/21   **(d)** 11/21

20.4 **(a)** 1/35   **(b)** 5/35;
      (a) 15/35   **(b)** 6/35   **(c)** 10/35   **(d)** 25/35

20.5 Without replacement: **(a)** 3/6   **(b)** 2/6   **(c)** 4/6;
      with replacement: **(a)** 12/27   **(b)** 8/27   **(c)** 19/27.

20.6 Without replacement: **(a)** $1/120$ **(b)** 0 **(c)** $10/120$
(d) $20/120$ **(e)** $45/120$ **(f)** $44/120$;
with replacement: **(a)** $1/5^5$ **(b)** $20/5^5$ **(c)** $160/5^5$
(d) $640/5^5$ **(e)** $1280/5^5$ **(f)** $(4/5)^5$.

20.7 **(a)** $1/945$ **(b)** $8/63$ **(c)** 0

20.8 **(a)** $1/10395$ **(b)** $16/231$ **(c)** $5/231$

20.9 $1/120$

20.10 $1/26$

20.11 **(a)** $225/784$ **(b)** $1/64$ **(c)** $\dfrac{(56)^3 - (8)(2^3)(7^3) + (28)(2^3)}{(56)^3}$

20.12 **(a)** $3/35$ **(b)** $24/35$ **(c)** $8/35$

SECTION 21

21.1 **(a)** $10^4, \dfrac{P(10, 4)}{10^4}$

(b) $n^r, \dfrac{P(n, r)}{n^r}$

21.2 **(a)** $\dfrac{C(10, 4)(4^4)(48)^6}{(52)^{10}}$

(b) $\dfrac{C(10, 5)(12)^5(40)^5}{(52)^{10}}$

(c) $\dfrac{C(10, 4)C(6, 5)(4^4)(12^5)(36)}{(52)^{10}}$

21.3 **(a)** $\dfrac{C(8, 3)(6^3)(30)^5}{(36)^8}$

(b) $\dfrac{C(10, 2)(2^2)(34)^8}{(36)^{10}}$

(c) $\dfrac{C(10, 4)C(6, 3)C(3, 2)(6^4)(4^3)(3^2)}{(36)^{10}} = \dfrac{10!}{4!3!2!} \cdot \dfrac{6^4 \cdot 4^3 \cdot 3^2}{(36)^{10}}$

21.4 **(a)** $P(9, 6)$ **(b)** 9^6 **(c)** $4 \cdot 9^5$

21.5 **(a)** $1/10!$ **(b)** $1/n!$

21.6 **(a)** $3!(50)!$ **(b)** $5!(48)!$ **(c)** $k!(52 - k + 1)!$

(d) $1/442, 1/54145, \dfrac{k!(52 - k + 1)!}{(52)!}$

21.7 **(a)** $C(52, 5)$ **(b)** $\dfrac{4C(13, 2)(13)^3}{C(52, 5)}$ **(c)** $\dfrac{C(13, 3)C(13, 2)}{C(52, 5)}$

21.8 **(a)** $C(52, 13)$ **(b)** $\dfrac{4^{13}}{C(52, 13)}$

(c) $\dfrac{C(13, 4)C(13, 5)C(13, 3)C(13, 1)}{C(52, 13)}$

(d) $C(4, 3)C(4, 2)C(4, 3)C(4, 2)C(4, 1)C(4, 2)$

21.9 **(a)** $4!$ **(b)** $4!\,C(6, 4)$

21.10 **(a)** $\dfrac{(18)!}{3!4!5!6!}$ **(b)** $\dfrac{(18)!}{3!4!5!6!} \cdot C(25, 18)$

21.11 **(a)** $2(4!)^2$ **(b)** $5(4!)^2$ **(c)** $5(4!)^2$ **(d)** $12(6!)$

21.12 **(a)** $1/33,\ 16/33,\ 16/33$

(b) $\dfrac{3}{(n - 1)(n - 3)},\ \dfrac{6(n - 4)}{(n - 1)(n - 3)},\ \dfrac{(n - 4)(n - 6)}{(n - 1)(n - 3)}$

21.13 **(a)** $\dfrac{(2n)(2n - 2)(2n - 4) \cdot\ \cdots\ \cdot (2n - [4r - 2])}{(2n)(2n - 1)(2n - 2) \cdot\ \cdots\ \cdot (2n - [2r - 1])}$

(b) $\dfrac{C(2r, 2)(2n)(2n - 2)(2n - 4) \cdot\ \cdots\ \cdot (2n - [4r - 4])}{(2n)(2n - 1)(2n - 2) \cdot\ \cdots\ \cdot (2n - [2r - 1])}$

(c) $\dfrac{C(2r, 2)C(2r - 2, 2)(2n)(2n - 2)(2n - 4)(2n - 6) \cdots\ \cdots \cdot (2n - [4r - 6])}{(2n)(2n - 1)(2n - 2) \cdot\ \cdots\ \cdot (2n - [2r - 1])}$

21.14 **(A)** **(a)** $1/(1 \cdot 3 \cdot 5 \cdot 7 \cdot 9 \cdot 11 \cdot 13 \cdot 15)$

(b) $8!/(1 \cdot 3 \cdot 5 \cdot 7 \cdot 9 \cdot 11 \cdot 13 \cdot 15)$

(c) $\dfrac{C(8, 4)(8!)^2}{(16)!}$

(B) **(a)** $1/[1 \cdot 3 \cdot 5 \cdot 7 \cdot\ \cdots\ \cdot (2n - 5)(2n - 3)(2n - 1)]$

(b) $n!/[1 \cdot 3 \cdot 5 \cdot 7 \cdot\ \cdots\ \cdot (2n - 5)(2n - 3)(2n - 1)]$

(c) $\dfrac{C(n, n/2)(n!)^2}{(2n)!}$

(C) **(a)** $1/[1 \cdot 3 \cdot 5 \cdot 7 \cdot\ \cdots\ \cdot (2n - 5)(2n - 3)(2n - 1)]$

(b) $n!/[1 \cdot 3 \cdot 5 \cdot 7 \cdot\ \cdots\ \cdot (2n - 5)(2n - 3)(2n - 1)]$

(c) 0

21.15 **(a)** $441/3025$ **(b)** $1/144$

(c) $\dfrac{(1320)^3 - 12 \cdot 3^3 \cdot (110)^3 + C(12, 2) \cdot 6^3 \cdot 10^3 - C(12, 3) \cdot 6^3}{(1320)^3}$

SECTION 22

22.1 **(a)** $\dfrac{C(12, 8)}{2^{12}}$ **(b)** $\dfrac{C(12, 9)}{2^{12}}$ **(c)** $\dfrac{C(20, 18)}{2^{20}}$

22.2 **(a)** $\dfrac{3920}{4^8}$ **(b)** $\dfrac{448}{4^8}$ **(c)** $\dfrac{1568}{4^8}$

22.3 $15!C(40, 15)$

22.4 $C(41, 30), \dfrac{C(40, 30)}{C(41, 30)}, \dfrac{C(29, 18)}{C(41, 30)}$

22.5 $C(16, 13), \dfrac{C(12, 9)}{C(16, 13)}$

22.6 $C(44, 25), \dfrac{C(24, 5)}{C(44, 25)}$

22.7 $1/6^3$

22.8 $1/56$

22.9 (a) $6/56$ (b) $30/56$ (c) $20/56$

22.10 $(5/6)^6, (5/6)^5, \dfrac{15 \cdot 5^4}{6^6}, \dfrac{20 \cdot 5^3}{6^6}, \dfrac{15 \cdot 5^2}{6^6}, 5/6^5, 1/6^6$

22.11 (a) $(9/10)^{10}$ (b) $(9/10)^9$ (c) $1 - (9/10)^{10}$

 (d) $\dfrac{C(10, k) \cdot 9^{10-k}}{10^{10}}$

22.12 (a) $(51/52)^{52}$ (b) $1 - (51/52)^{52}$
 (c) $(51/52)^{52} + (51/52)^{51}$
 (d) $1 - [(51/52)^{52} + (51/52)^{51} + (1/2)(51/52)^{51}]$

Index

Distributions of particles into
   cells, 114
Dividend, 12
Divisibility tests, 20, 21
Division
  by zero, 5
  in R_n, 76
  of integers, 4, 11
  of matrices, 97
  of rationals, 6
  theorems on, 11, 12
Division algorithm, 12
Divisor, 12
  common, 22
  greatest common, 22, 45, 77,
   78
Divisors of an integer, 11
  algebra of, 31
  number of, 42
  product of, 58, 78
  sum of, 54, 59, 78

Elevator problem, 113, 130
Empty set, 105
E-prime, 40
Equally likely outcomes, 103
Equations
  linear, 79
  quadratic, 79, 80, 82
Eratosthenes, sieve of, 34, 35
Euclid, 22, 34, 56
Euclid's algorithm, 23
Euler, L., 56
Even number, 14
Events, 104
Experiment, 103

Factorial, 38, 123
Factorization of integers
  canonical or standard, 37
  into a product of primes, 36
  mosaic, 49
  nonunique, 38, 40
  unique, 36
Factorization of quadratic equations, 82
Factors, 11

Fermat's Last Theorem, 73
Fraction or rational number, 6
Fundamental Theorem of Arith-
  metic, 36

Goldbach's conjecture, 39
Greatest common divisor, 22, 45
  in R_n, 77, 78

Hindus, 19

Inequality relations, 8, 9
Integers, 3
  composite, 34
  even, 14
  in decimal system, 15
  in different bases, 15
  modulo-n, 70
  negative, 3
  number of divisors of, 42
  odd, 14
  operations on, 3
  positive, 3
  prime, 14, 34
  product of divisors of, 58
  properties of, 3
  relatively prime, 22
  sum of divisors of, 54, 59
Least common multiple, 28, 45
  in R_n, 77, 78
Linear equations, 79
  in R_n, 79, 80
  roots of, 79, 80
Linear factors, 85

Magic number, 58
Matching problems, 117, 132
Matrices, algebra of, 86
Matrix
  determinant of, 95
  unit, 90
  zero, 88
Mersenne prime, 56
Modular systems, 63
Modulo-n, 70
Mosaic factorization, 49